PRESENTED TO

Harold Gaehnacht,

DATE: _Oct '67_

SOUTHERN CALIFORNIA EDISON COMPANY

The Story of Big Creek

Diagrammatic map of Southern California Edison Company's Big Creek-San Joaquin River hydro-electric development.

THE STORY
OF BIG CREEK

BY DAVID H. REDINGER

Angelus Press, Los Angeles, California

TO

the one who has really stood by through

all the years of our married life—

MY WIFE

Foreword

THIS IS A BIOGRAPHY *of a great engineering project, written by David H. Redinger, Resident Engineer, whose life and career were builded into the Big Creek hydroelectric project. This story was not written for publication as a book but rather as a report and history for the records of Southern California Edison Company. It has seemed to us, however, that it is a document of too great significance to be buried in the archives of our company.*

What is its significance? It is an outstanding story of the golden age of American development. Here again is a stirring and inspiring example of the work of free men, self-reliant men, men who did not wait to have society or government underwrite the risk.

Today, Americans perform equally great miracles of construction but too often we turn to "government" to underwrite the risk, parroting a stultifying statement to the effect that the undertaking is "too big for private enterprise."

This is a story of the older America—a brilliant example of the courage and vision of men who never thought of asking government to underwrite their risk because it was "too big" for them as private citizens.

From the earliest conception of the project of John Eastwood, through the building of a railroad into the High Sierra in 157 days, to unprecedented road-building, tunneling, dam-building, "snowed-in" construction camps at high altitudes, and similar unsung exploits, this is a story not of "heroic" men but of just straight-thinking, hard-working Americans of the old school.

W. C. Mullendore

Table of Contents

List of illustrations

Preface

IT HAS BEEN SAID that God never intended Southern California to be anything but desert; man made it what it is. That this is true is borne out in David H. Redinger's story of how man harnessed a great watershed so that the water flow should not be dissipated in floods but be conserved to water the lands of fertile valleys and provide electric power for all those living in the region.

In spite of all the other natural benefits of the area, the absence of close water resources has probably had more influence on the development of Central and Southern California than any other single factor.

Because of this lack, man has had to go far afield to find water for domestic, agricultural and industrial use, as well as water for the development of electric power. In the early days the few rivers in the area—the Santa Ana, Mill Creek, San Gabriel, Kern, Tule and Kaweah—were utilized for this latter purpose. Lack of storage capacity, however, meant that the plants on these rivers must depend upon seasonal rainfall, and it soon became apparent that the demand for electric power far exceeded this limited supply.

In 1911 the Pacific Light and Power Corporation undertook one of the greatest water power developments in the world—the Big Creek-San Joaquin project in the High Sierra of Central California. It is this project with which Mr. Redinger was concerned for many years.

This tremendous development, which was brought to its present stage of completion in 1929 by the Southern California Edison Company, which absorbed Pacific Light and Power Corporation in 1917, is situated in Fresno County, about sixty miles northeast of the city of Fresno and approximately 270 miles from Los Angeles. It is a composite of three major artificial lakes created by the construction of six dams, eight tunnels—the longest the 13.5-mile Ward Tunnel—and a series of five power houses whose sixteen units utilize the water from a drainage area of approximately 1,050 square miles.

The initial work, begun by Pacific Light and Power Corporation, consisted of construction of three dams which formed Huntington Lake reservoir, Powerhouses No. 1 and No. 2 and the 248-mile steel tower high-voltage transmission line to Los Angeles. Powerhouses No. 1 and No. 2 originally were constructed with two units in each plant, giving the Big Creek project a total initial capacity of 91,188 horsepower. The two 150,000 volt transmission lines were an outstanding feature of this installation as they were of the highest voltage and greatest length constructed to that time. The voltage of the lines later (1923) was increased to 220,000 volts, again establishing a precedent in long distance high-voltage transmission.

After the Edison Company absorbed Pacific Light and Power Corporation, new plants and new units in existing plants were required to enable the company to keep abreast of the power demands of the area it served. Big Creek system additions included 61,686 horsepower capacity in Powerhouse No. 1; 45,594 horsepower capacity in Powerhouse No. 2; the construction of Powerhouse No. 3 with three units totaling 132,759 horsepower; and the completion of Powerhouse No. 8 with 77,778 horsepower capacity. These additions were made between 1917 and 1929. In May of 1948 the installation of a fourth unit in Powerhouse No. 3 was completed.

The key project of the development of the Big Creek-San Joaquin River hydro-electric power resources was the construction of Ward Tunnel, formerly designated as the Florence Lake Tunnel, between Florence and Huntington Lakes. The installation of additional units in Powerhouses No. 1 and No. 2 and the construction of No. 3 and No. 8 necessitated the utilization of water that was available in large volume in the upper drainage areas of the South Fork of the San Joaquin River. This drainage area, however, was separated from the Huntington Lake reservoir area by Kaiser Ridge, a barrier of solid granite nearly eleven miles in width and reaching an elevation of 9,300 feet. The drainage area beyond the barrier was tapped by the construction of Ward Tunnel through Kaiser Ridge. The tunnel is fifteen feet in width, fifteen feet high and is built on a mean grade of 17.2 feet per mile. Florence Lake storage reservoir was created by the construction of a multiple arch dam 3,200 feet in length with a maximum height of 147 feet, at a small natural lake on the South Fork of the San Joaquin river.

Additional storage capacity was provided subsequently with the construction of Shaver Lake reservoir. Diversion of water to Shaver Lake is through a conduit from Dam No. 2 at Huntington Lake, discharging into the channel of the North Fork of Stevenson Creek and thence into Shaver Lake.

The water stored in Shaver Lake is utilized through Powerhouse No. 2A, adjacent to Powerhouse No. 2. Supplementing the supply of water into Shaver Lake from Florence and Huntington Lakes, diversion works were constructed to bring the waters of Mono Creek and Bear Creek into Ward Tunnel. Powerhouse No. 2A, placed in operation in 1928, has two units totaling 124,713 horsepower capacity, and operates under a total head of 2,418 feet, one of the highest operating heads in America.

The creation of this vast water power development has brought many benefits to Central and Southern California. As a source of electricity, it supplies 428,000 kilowatts of the Edison Company's combined hydroelectric and fuel-electric generating capacity of 1,582,855 kilowatts.

It further acts as a water conservation and flood prevention measure. The water that makes the electricity eventually is used for irrigation of the great San Joaquin Valley, the largest agricultural region in California. The development program likewise opened to the public, through the construction of numerous roads, a vast mountain playground otherwise virtually inaccessible.

I

Introduction

MANY OF MY FRIENDS have suggested that I put on paper the story of Big Creek, and my association of thirty years with the project bearing its name. Although I had been considering such a task for some time, I did not make a final decision to write the story until impetus was given me by Harry J. Bauer, Chairman of the Board of Directors of the Southern California Edison Company.

The name "Big Creek" includes not only the small settlement where our field headquarters have always been located, but the entire project, covering hundreds of square miles.

A resumé of my own background may afford an explanation as to how I became associated with the project.

A few days before graduation from the University of Kansas with a degree in civil engineering in 1911, I received a temporary appointment on a United States Government investigation in Alaska, involving the Bering River Coal Fields. This area, along with Controller Bay, formed the basis of much controversy in Washington at that time. The appointment came by telegram from the Commisisoner of the United States General Land Office, Washington, D.C., and I must say it gave me one of the greatest thrills of a life-time. I still have the original message. Since the appointment came shortly before commencement, a special examination had to be arranged and given quickly to allow me to meet the June 1 sailing from Seattle. I have always been grateful to

Dean F. O. Marvin for the consideration he extended in making it possible for me to take advantage of a most unusual opportunity, particularly for a new college graduate.

My qualifications for work with coal arose out of my experience in the five-year period between my high school and college courses, which I spent in and around the mines and coal fields of Colorado. A large portion of this time was spent with an uncle, H. C. Nicholls, who operated several mines in the southern part of that state. Through this association I came in contact with his mining engineer, M. S. Hibbard, retained for the engineering necessary for the proper functioning of such underground work. I was assigned to assist him on each of his monthly trips to the mines. Eventually, I was spending all of my time in this manner, and accompanied Mr. Hibbard on trips to many of the large mines in other parts of the state. One day I made the decision to return to my native state and enter college. Mr. Hibbard maintained contact with me during the four years I was in college, and made possible my appointment on the Alaskan work, when he was given full responsibility for that project.

Upon completing the field work in Alaska, the crew engaged there, with the exception of one man, returned to Seattle, where final details were completed in the office. George Parks, a member of the party, remained in Alaska, and in due time was appointed Governor by President Coolidge.

On my return to Seattle, like many others from the North, I made my headquarters at the Frey Hotel, which had just been completed. This hostelry seemed to be a favorite rendezvous for many of the Alaska "sourdoughs." At the hotel I made the acquaintance of H. P. Banks, a chemical engineer who had also just returned from Alaska, and this chance acquaintance developed into a warm friendship which has continued to the present time. It was he who was responsible for my coming to Big Creek.

In the course of several weeks, Mr. Banks mentioned that a large hydroelectric development was being started in the High Sierra of California, and that a college mate of his was connected with its construction. Mr. Banks contemplated going to the job himself, and wondered if I would be interested. Not having been to California, and knowing nothing whatever about hydroelectric development, I was eager for such a chance, particularly since my government assignment was drawing to a close. Midsummer of 1912 found both Mr. Banks and me at Big Creek—he as a chemist in charge of the cement-testing laboratory, and I as a transit man. On my way down from Seattle I had thought I would look over the Big Creek job, and after a few months probably go on to other "pastures." Little did I realize that the year 1947 would find me still keenly interested in and enjoying my connection with the project. My good friend Mr. Banks spent several years in the Edison Right-of-Way Department in Los Angeles and then returned to Seattle, where today he is playing a major role in a successful manufacturing concern.

After having spent a large part of my life in close association with the development of such a large project in all its phases, and having seen it grow from nothing to what it is today, is it any wonder I have formed more than just a "bread and butter" attachment for these things built by man—to say nothing of the natural grandeur of the scenery which is so much a part of them?

D. H. REDINGER

Big Creek, Calif.
1949

II
John S. Eastwood

A NATURAL QUESTION one might raise concerns the identity of the man who first recognized the power possibilities in this region and, therefore, is responsible for the birth of the Big Creek-San Joaquin Hydroelectric Project. Surely credit for this should go to John S. Eastwood, engineer, who made numerous trips into the Big Creek country—his first, according to Mrs. Eastwood, in 1886.

Mr. Eastwood was born in Scott County, Minnesota. On August 13, 1924, at the age of sixty-seven years, he was drowned or died of a heart attack while swimming in Kings River. At the time of his death he was investigating the Pine Flat Project below Trimmer, California. In one of his notes, written to General W. H. Hart in July, 1902, he described himself as a "railway engineer of quite wide experience." In 1884 he had made a reconnaissance for a railway from Fresno to Pine Ridge, which is about ten miles below Shaver Lake, and was running lines for power development during 1900 and 1901. Besides being an engineer, Mrs. Eastwood has informed us, her husband loved the mountains and was a keen student of forestry—so much so that by placing his hand on a tree in the dark he could name its kind. She has written that during the latter part of 1886 and for a year or more following, Mr. Eastwood was a timber expert for a large lumber company, for which he also located and built tramways for saw mills.

He had become much interested in electric power transmission,

4

and saw the possibility of developing power for Fresno. In 1894 he made the first examinations of the ground of the North Fork of the San Joaquin, and during the spring of 1895 the San Joaquin Electric Company was organized, with him as vice president, chief engineer, and superintendent. The capital stock was $800,000.00, all of which was subscribed by seven directors—six of them subscribing $500.00 each, and Mr. Eastwood $797,000.00. The plant was finished April 14, 1896. Mrs. Eastwood writes that she had the honor of touching the button that put the great dynamos and machinery in motion in the substation at Fresno, while Mr. Eastwood was listening in over the telephone at North Fork, thirty-seven miles away. At that time this was the longest transmission line in the world. This must have been the original Crane Valley Plant, alongside of which now stands the A. G. Wishon Power House of the Pacific Gas & Electric Company, on the shore of Kerckhoff Lake. In a grassy plot in front of the old building, for all to see, stands one of the first generators, with a copper placque indicating it as such. The plant was in operation from June 1896 to 1910, making it the forerunner of the present large system.

In 1914 Mr. Eastwood was requested to write the early history of the San Joaquin Electric Company. It contains, among many others, this interesting paragraph:

"Shortly after the completion of the plant, a longer distance of transmisison was made in Utah, which was again exceeded by us building to Hanford, a distance of seventy-nine miles. In this connection, it is a pleasure to state that I did all of the preliminary work in what is now the largest plant on the Pacific Coast, the longest transmission in the world, and the highest head in the world, that which is used for the large plant, the Big Creek development of the Pacific Light & Power Corporation." (The predecessor of the Southern California Edison Company.)

With respect to the Big Creek Project, Mrs. Eastwood has written that she cannot give the exact date when her husband made the surveys, but she is definite on this—that he had studied and investigated the water power possibilities of the Big Creek country before the San Joaquin Light & Power Company went into the hands of a receiver in the fall of 1899. He had kept the knowledge of his investigation to himself, as he wanted to be sure of his water findings. When the San Joaquin Light & Power Company failed, he remarked to Mrs. Eastwood, who says that she was a sharer in his secret, "I could organize a new company, and could have a much greater power project than the San Joaquin Light & Power Company, but I don't think it would be right." So he offered the results of his investigations to the succeeding company—the Pacific Light and Power Corporation—and merged all his interests in the Big Creek Project, going out of the San Joaquin Company without one cent.

He was in the mountains in 1900, five weeks at one time, making surveys, looking into the possibilities of a greater power project in the Big Creek country. In the Fresno Bee of May 8, 1941, "Fresno's Yesterday's Forty Years Ago," there appeared this item:

> "John S. Eastwood, Civil Engineer of the Mammoth Power Company of San Jose, had a large crew of men in the mountains east of Fresno, where they were making a survey for a tunnel and flume."

In September, 1902, he organized a survey party, and from his files I quote from a letter written to W. G. Kerckhoff about one month after he had the party in the field:

> "Big Creek, October 7, 1902.
> It gives me great pleasure to inform you that I have completed the surveys for a tunnel line to the junction of Pitman and Big Creeks, and I can place before you the most remarkable power project yet presented."

Power House No. 1, of the Southern California Edison Company, now stands at the junction of the two creeks which Mr. Eastwood mentions in the above letter.

In the party of September, 1902, was A. Emory Wishon, who, until his death in 1948, was executive vice-president of the Pacific Gas & Electric Company. In one of his letters to me, with reference to this particular crew, Mr. Wishon states there were two such parties, one being headed by Mr. Eastwood, the other by Louie Manuel. The surveys were described as starting at Shaver Lake, and continuing to what is now Huntington Lake, where lines and levels were run to determine quickly the available storage capacity of the reservoir, and where cross-sections were taken of the proposed Dams 1 and 2. The surveys also included the running of a line over Kaiser Pass to determine the length of tunnel necessary to bring in the South Fork of the San Joaquin River. This idea was carried out in later years when the Florence Lake Tunnel, later named Ward Tunnel, was driven, connecting Florence and Huntington Lakes.

Mr. Wishon also stated that he walked with Mr. Eastwood to the top of Kaiser Mountain at a point overlooking the Big Creek country, the South Fork of the San Joaquin, and Jose Basin. Mr. Eastwood spent several hours describing to Mr. Wishon, then just a youngster, the full project he had in mind—and, as far as our present Power House No. 2 is concerned there have been few changes from Mr. Eastwood's original ideas—but from there down the canyon, the project has been developed differently than was contemplated by him.

It is interesting to learn that one of Mr. Eastwood's plans, as related by Mr. Wishon, involved driving a shaft through the solid granite of Kerckhoff Dome, to be lined with light steel filled in behind with concrete. It was his thought at the time that such a shaft, to serve as a penstock, would be a great saving, and something entirely original.

One day during the same period, Mr. Wishon brought into camp a piece of marble he had found in the Big Creek Canyon, and showed it to Mr. Eastwood. The latter became very enthusiastic over it, and spent several days and evenings sketching a power house which he planned to build with the local product. This sample was taken from the site known today as the Wishon Marble Quarry, located about midway between our Big Creek No. 1 and No. 2 Plants. For many years, the Wishons faithfully made the necessary annual assessment work on this claim.

A. G. Wishon, at the time he was president of the San Joaquin Light and Power Corporation, in a letter dated January 3, 1929, stated that Mr. Eastwood was never on the payroll of his company but on that of the Pacific Light & Power Corporation instead. According to Mrs. Eastwood, he received only a small salary—just sufficient for living expenses—during the several years he was engaged on the preliminary work of the Big Creek Project, because the future seemed bright. At last he lost everything.

During the summer of 1923 I had the pleasure of taking Mr. Eastwood over a large part of the Big Creek work completed at that time. He was a quiet, unassuming man, keenly interested in everything he saw on this, his first trip since the construction was started. The place where he wanted to make his longest stop was at Stevenson Creek, on our Lower Road. He stood speechless for a while, looking up at the 1,600 foot cliff above us, and then commented that he was just thinking how easily he had just reached this point, as compared to a trip many years before on which he had such difficulty getting in and out.

Mr. Eastwood became interested in dam construction, and is credited with having developed the theory of the Multiple Arch type, like that at Florence Lake.

The naming of Kerchoff Dome, in honor of W. G. Kerchoff, is credited to Mr. Eastwood. It is most unfortunate that nothing in this whole area has ever been named for the man who had the courage, vision and ability to recognize the power possibilities in this part of the Sierra. His brother made a similar comment to me when I called on him in Fresno a few years ago.

III

San Joaquin & Eastern Railroad

WITH THE ARRIVAL of the years 1910 and 1911, the Pacific Light & Power Corporation found itself faced with serving a rapidly increasing population, and something had to be done to take care of the load which was likewise increasing throughout Southern California. Some idea of this growth and development may be had when it is recalled that the population of Los Angeles city was 105,000 in 1905, 500,000 in 1914, and 1,810,000 in 1944.

The company realized that additional generating capacity for electricity must be provided to meet the demands of the electric railways and commercial needs, since its plants were already operating at practically full output. Seventy-five per cent of their capacity was steam-generated, and it was desirable to replace it with hydroelectric power, which could be supplied then at less cost. In any large power system good operating practice requires a fairly even division between steam and hydro plants to insure dependable service. When the hydro plant gets into trouble—and this does happen—the steam plant must be called upon to make up the difference. The advantage was apparent, too, of the less variable cost for water power generation, as compared to the more variable and increasing cost of steam power produced with fuel oil. Today the cost per barrel of fuel oil has risen to a price more than double that prevailing in 1911 and 1912.

In 1911 the operating capacity of the Pacific Light & Power

system was about 75,000 h.p., distributed among ten plants, including Redondo Steam Station. It is interesting to compare that with today's capacity of the Southern California Edison System, which is approximately 2,000,000 h.p. from a total of twenty-four hydro plants, four steam plants, and one diesel plant.

To provide additional power, negotiations were entered into with the San Joaquin Light and Power Corporation whereby the Pacific Light and Power Corporation acquired the rights, filings, etc., necessary to proceed with the development of the Big Creek Project. Practically all the capital stock of the latter corporation was owned by Henry E. Huntington, who also owned the entire capital stock of the Los Angeles Railway Corporation.

One of the first problems encountered involved transportation, as the site of the proposed development was in the Sierra Nevada mountains fifty miles from the nearest railroad. Hauling by twelve or fourteen mule teams was impractical for several reasons—the early completion desired, distances involved, and steep grades to be encountered in the handling of enormous tonnage.

The decision was made by the Pacific Light & Power Corporation to build a railroad, and the San Joaquin & Eastern Railroad Company was organized as a subsidiary. A contract was made with the Stone & Webster Construction Company of Boston, and authority given to proceed with construction on January 26, 1912. Prior to this date, though, about December 1, 1911, a reconnaissance party was in the vicinity of Friant, seeking the best route through the foothills to reach Auberry. At that time Friant was, and it still is, the terminus of a branch of the Southern Pacific, and is now the site of huge Friant Dam, recently completed by the United States Bureau of Reclamation. The location selected for the junction with the Southern Pacific was named "El Prado", and was six miles south of Friant and eighteen from Fresno.

Ground was broken on February 5, 1912, and the last spike

driven on July 10, completing the fifty-six miles to Big Creek. Building this much standard gauge railroad in one hundred fifty-seven days constituted a record for such work. The survey crews had to hustle to keep ahead of construction, as time was of the essence after the job was once started.

There was nothing available for such construction in the way of the modern equipment we have today—such as tractor-type shovels, bulldozers, motor-operated graders and scrapers, dump trucks, carryalls, etc.; consequently, all work had to be done by team and scraper, wheelbarrows, and hand drilling. There was not even one of the old railroad-type steam shovels used, except for a few dipperfuls on the Big Creek end by one being moved through to "The Basin" (Huntington Lake). All drilling for blasting, instead of being done with the present-day type of hammer drills, was done by hand, with the well-known single and double-jack methods. The former is done by one man holding his own drill with one hand and wielding the sledge with the other. The latter method involves two men, one holding the drill with one or both hands while the sledge hammer is slung by the other man. Woe be unto the hammer wielder, too, if he missed the drill. A real old-time double-jacker never missed, but until he had proved his skill to the satisfaction of his helper, the latter might use a handle to hold the drill, for his own safety, although such practice was considered to be only for amateurs.

Old records reveal some other interesting things. The work was carried on seven days per week, and at least ten hours per day. The maximum number of men on the payroll at one time was 1,270, in March. The average from January through May was about 800 men. The average wage paid was between twenty-seven and twenty-eight cents per hour. The turn-over was large, as men did not have to look far for work. It was unusual for a man to have more than one hundred hours time in a month, and timekeepers did not have to worry much about classifications, which consisted almost entirely of laborers, teamsters and drillers.

There were eleven hundred curves in the railroad, the maximum curvature being sixty degrees. The sharpness of these curves limited the use of both passenger and freight cars to those thirty-six feet in length. There was always a notation on requisitions for material and supplies that shipments must be made in cars not exceeding that length. Occasionally, there would be an error and some shipper would get his order into a longer car, thereby requiring the cargo to be reloaded at Fresno or El Prado.

The need for such respect for the sharp curves was impressed upon me while on my first trip to Big Creek. It was said to be about the first regular run, and we left El Prado in the forenoon of August 12, 1912, arriving at Big Creek at 3:00 a.m. the following day. The train literally felt its way above Auberry, but in spite of the care taken, several car steps were either damaged or torn off by overhanging rocks on curves.

Standard rod engines were used between the valley and Auberry, the division point, but because of steep grades above—maximum 5.6 per cent—geared locomotives, Shays and Climaxes, were used between Auberry and Big Creek. These geared engines, pulling their respective trains on the climb up the mountain, would make a terrible fuss, the noise being comparable to the New York Central's "Century" roaring through the Mohawk Valley; but where the "Century" would be making eighty to one hundred miles per hour, the Shay or Climax might be going five or six.

For some years, until 1926, railroad tickets read "To Cascada," but mail would be addressed "Big Creek," although they were one and the same place. John B. Miller, then Chairman of the Board of the Southern California Edison Company, was responsible for dropping the name "Cascada." He preferred "Big Creek" which to him was more typical of the country's ruggedness and the big outdoors.

There was some confusion, also, in the local mail service, since there was a postoffice, "Cascada," in California.

The railroad was the principal means of transportation for many years for the employees and their families, and the general public was also served through a total of twenty-two stations. Business was so brisk for a long time that the Big Creek depot was open day and night—a distinction usually enjoyed only by large city stations.

The main highway to the San Joaquin Valley was not oiled in those days, and was closed by winter conditions usually from November to March or April, depending upon severity of the winter and earliness of the following spring. Due to heavy snow in January, 1913, there was a period of nineteen days when there was no train in or out of Big Creek. Several miles of track had to be cleared of three to five feet of snow to release a locomotive snowbound below Big Creek. One hundred fifty men did the job by hand. Some were using wooden shovels, hurriedly improvised. One man broke his, and, there being no replacement at hand, the foreman sent him on ahead to another group as "straw boss". Such quick promotion was the cue for the "accidental" breaking of other shovels to such an extent that methods had to be changed forthwith. Local telephone communication with the train dispatcher at Auberry was disrupted, and Roy Walker, station agent at Big Creek throughout the life of the railroad except for a few months, walked five miles to West Portal to make contact. He took two train orders before failure of the telephone line between him and the dispatcher, and remained at his post for five days until an engine came from Auberry, there being no communication in the meantime. During his sojourn he was furnished meals by a construction family living in a tent nearby, and to his utter amazement, they were served on Haviland china.

Often referred to as "slow, jerky and expensive," the San Joaquin & Eastern occupied a place unique in the annals of railroads. A trip over it was long to be remembered, especially if one were at all subject to *mal de mer*. There were other things more pleasant. One could board the train at the Southern Pacific Depot in Fresno early in the morning—and for those desiring something special, a parlor car was available in later years. If it were crowded at the start—and it frequently was—the passengers would thin out rapidly and move to another car when the conductor called for the extra fare. For summer use there were open cars with canopy tops, called "Bleachers". Fair speed could be attained between El Prado and Auberry, where the geared locomotives would replace the rod type for the three thousand foot climb to Big Creek. Shortly after leaving El Prado the conductor would ascertain the number of box lunches required, and these would be put aboard on arrival at Stevenson Creek. It was interesting to see how quickly the dogs along the way learned the daily schedule, and were on hand for tid-bits thrown out by passengers.

As the train struggled up the grades, one could look several thousand feet below and see the San Joaquin River winding like a shiny ribbon through the canyon. When one grew tired of this, there were lofty peaks to admire, snow-capped in winter, which would begin to peek out in the distance, and near the journey's end there were the lovely water falls at the base of Kerchoff Dome. Such a delight it was, when sufficient altitude had been made, to be among the grand old pines, to enjoy the mild aroma—such as can come only from them—wafted through the open car windows. Now and then there would be a smell resembling witch hazel, from bear clover—so-called, it is said, because it is not clover and the bears do not like it. It belongs to the rose family. What a relief too, after having left the hot valley—air conditioning, of course had not arrived—to feel and breathe the pure, cool air which only mountains can supply.

A favorite stunt of each conductor, and one which afforded amusement for the passengers, was to leave the train at the beginning of a long, sharp curve near Webstone, walk across the neck, and get aboard on the far side.

The supervisory personnel, headed by W. H. Dresser and H. L. Wheeler, would scoot over the rails in special equipment, of which there were several pieces, each consisting of a touring car body fitted with flanged steel wheels. A roller coaster could offer no more thrills for the uninitiated than the first trip on one of these contraptions. There was much uncertainty of the thing's making the sharp curves, as reflected by the foot pressure on the front floor boards. One's fears would be relieved but little, if on some of the curves he happened to relax enough to even glance down into a deep and precipitous canyon.

In the early summer, passengers interested in wild flowers would have a treat through the foothills when "baby blue eyes," gold poppies, "snow in the mountains," Mariposa lilies, and blue lupine were at their best. Further along there would be the Judas Tree, or "red bud," and near Hairpin they could see a few bushes of the lovely Carpenteria California. A ranger of the local Forest Service, reputed to speak authoritatively on wild flowers of the area, says this location, including Tollhouse Grade, is the only place in the world where this rare flower grows. Besides its fame for rarity, it has the further distinction of small seeds—15,600,000 to the pound. Late in the fall, Indians could be seen harvesting their acorns and storing them in grass-covered containers high on stilts for safety against birds and animals.

Although probably not recorded in the archives, it should be mentioned that the stork paid a visit on one trip. Conductor Tucker and one of his brakemen shared honors in "entertaining" the bird. Despite the improvised facilities, the principals could not have fared better in the maternity ward of a hospital.

Hundreds of thousands of tons of material and supplies, and many thousands of men, were transported during the busy life of the railroad. One year the freight receipts amounted to over $1,000,000. The usual freight train would consist of four cars for one engine, and seven with a double-header.

With completion of the major construction in 1929, there was not much to foresee in the way of freight, express or passenger traffic, all of which had been dwindling for some time. Automobiles had been coming into more general use, and were supplemented by a bus line operated between the Big Creek area and Fresno by W. R. Miles. Even the mail contract had forsaken the railroad for the faster bus service. Eventually—March 6, 1930—the bus line was taken over and operated by the railroad, until October 16, 1934, when it was sold to Fortier's, of Fresno, who have continued operation to the present. Rail service reached a stage where trains were being run only as often as was required under the franchise. I recall being picked up one day in the vicinity of West Portal. The crew was most accommodating, even between stations, in view of such light traffic. The train consisted of an engine and caboose, and there was only one passenger when I got aboard. I was twitting the conductor, Walter Low, about his light pay load, and he pointed to a carton containing half a dozen two-inch pipe valves which was the only freight item.

The inevitable arrived, and the railroad was abandoned in 1933. On August 15 the last train, consisting of an engine and caboose, made its last run in and out of Big Creek, with Ernest Root at the throttle. It can really be said that Spike Meehan, who took the first locomotive into Big Creek, then "Cascada," on July 13, 1912, also handled the throttle on the last run, since it was he who, as hostler at Auberry, had prepared the engine for the final trip. There was nothing unusual the day the last run was made to herald the passing of this railroad, unique in many ways, which had played a major role in the development of one of the world's largest power projects.

It required some time for the Big Creek residents to become accustomed to the quietness of the canyon, no longer echoing with the train's whistle, so welcome for many years, or with the grinding of wheels on the distant curves. The reaction of some was in direct contrast to the thrill and excitement manifested on the day—twenty-one years before—when the first locomotive had noisily labored its way alongside the little station, which at that time consisted of one tent.

All rolling stock, rail and ties, were removed and sold, and subsequently the right-of-way reverted to the land owners, the largest being the United States Government. The greater portion now serves as a public road, particularly between Hairpin and Indian Mission. Between Indian Mission and Shaver Crossing where it joins the State Highway, the upper portion is impassable in winter. To the passer-by nothing remains but an occasional station sign or water tank as a reminder of what was once a most unique railroad.

Shay gear-type locomotive used on San Joaquin and Eastern Railroad. Conductor Barnett second from right.

S. J. & E. speeder used by railroad operating personnel.

Right: Powerhouse No. 1 with Kerckhoff Dome in the background.

Below: Powerhouse No. 2 in 1922.

IV

Initial Development

IN THE EARLY '90's, and long before the San Joaquin & Eastern
Railroad was thought of, the Fresno Flume & Irrigation Company, for its own operations at Shaver, extended the county
road north about two miles to what was known as Griffin's Shake
Camp. Following the surveys made in 1902 by Mr. Eastwood, the
San Joaquin Light & Power Corporation, under the direction of
A. G. Wishon, continued the road and completed it into Big Creek
in 1909, preparatory to starting development of the Big Creek Project themselves. The same year the J. G. White Company constructed for Wishon's company the present Pitman Creek weir, also one
across Big Creek. The latter had to be destroyed in 1912 when Dam
4 was built. These weirs, like all such structures, were for the purpose of securing data on stream flow, since such information is of
primary importance in connection with water power development.

So far, the plans of Wishon's company did not include a road to
The Basin (later named Huntington Lake), as it was contemplated
that freight and passengers would be transported by an incline
cableway. The ground clearing for this had already been done. Mr.
Wishon told me he made a special trip to Los Angeles to promote
the construction of a road about which there was disagreement
among the directors. His sales talk, apparently, had some effect,
and the present road was built in 1910, with an outfit consisting of
ten men, one team, a plow and a scraper. H. B. Howard and Charlie
Miller, with hand level and tape, were the engineers. Maximum

grade of 12% was intended, but due to the lack of full cooperation on the part of the directorate for a road of any kind, there resulted one much steeper stretch just above the "saddle" which remains a bugaboo to many motorists, and which can easily be identified on almost any hot day by cars stalled due to over-heating.

Negotiations had been completed for the Pacific Light & Power Corporation to take over, and contracts for designing and constructing what is known as "the initial development" were executed early in 1912 with the Stone & Webster Engineering Corporation, which was then building the railroad to Big Creek. Headquarters which had been established in Old Town, on the south bank of Pitman Creek, were moved to the present location, then called Camp 2, late in 1911. Bunk houses were being built, and the mess hall had been opened early in December.

The first automobile to reach Big Creek from Auberry, via Indian Mission, Stevenson Creek and Dawn, arrived on December 11, 1911, the occupants being S. L. Shuffleton, F. M. Thebo, Arthur F. Blight, A. C. Criddle, and Bill Wright. As far as Dawn, which became a station, the route traveled by this party was almost identical to that over which the railroad was built shortly thereafter. From Dawn the car came via Camp 6 over a newly constructed road which joined the present state highway at the foot of the Shaver grade. This junction is the beginning of what we now call our Lower Road.

The area which Big Creek occupies is said to have been used by Potter and Freeman as a sheep range in 1870-71, and was known as "Big Creek Flats." In 1902 when John Eastwood made his principal surveys, and up to the time of beginning development of the project, the area was called "Manzanita Park."

Some enlargement of headquarters was still under way when I arrived by train at three o'clock in the morning of August 13, 1912. In those days men carried their own bed rolls, or "bindles," and were known as "construction stiffs." Another favorite term for one's bed roll in construction parlance was "crumb pile"—from "crumb," which the soldiers of the first World War called "cootie." "Crumb boss" was the name for a caretaker around bunk houses, since he had to "ride herd" over the occupants, many of whom in those days were quite apt to be pediculous. "Bull cook" has become the more common name.

Because of the early hour of my arrival—dawn was breaking in the east—I crawled into a huge pile of shavings in the unfinished office building until six o'clock, when the mess hall triangle sounded "all out." After breakfast the "crumb boss" suggested I provide myself with a mattress, and directed me to the nearest barn, one-half mile distant, where I obtained a large armful of straw. He then assigned me to a bunk, of which there were three tiers around the inside of the bunk house. It is strange how quickly straw can harden in a bed where the only springs are boards. Being a greenhorn, I was happy to have one of the bottom bunks. After the first night I learned why the uppers were so much more desirable—in a lower, every time the fellow above moved or turned over, one got chaff and dirt in his face. The old and reliable Sibley stove in the center of the room not only furnished too much or too little heat, depending upon the location of the bunk, but served too, as a drier for all the damp or wet clothing hanging around. Outside plumbing thrived in all its glory, and no one can fully appreciate how cold water can be until he tries to wash in an outside trough at six A.M., with the thermometer hovering between "zero" and "freezing," making no particular effort to go higher. At such times it wasn't much of a disappointment to find the water line frozen.

After having contacted W. D. Shannon and Arthur Blight, construction and division engineer, respectively, I was assigned temporarily to the party headed by Harry Banks for work on Tunnel No. 2, which eventually would carry the water from Power House No. 1 to No. 2. Austin B. Mason was in direct charge as tunnel engineer, Harry Banks handled the transit, and H. B. Howard and I the tape, level rod and paint bucket.

Our job was to keep the tunnel crews driving in the proper direction and at the correct elevation. Nine adits, each providing two headings, or faces, were employed to expedite driving. An adit, the opposite of exit, may be thought of as a side entrance to a tunnel anywhere between two portals. An adit may be on the same grade as a tunnel, or at a steep angle. If vertical, or nearly so, it would be called a shaft. Since there were so many headings, and as the work was on a twenty-four hour basis, our party at times would be "run ragged" because blasting would occur at any hour. It was our job to go in after each round was fired, to give direction and grade, or elevation, for drilling the next. Like a train crew, we were on a call basis.

Along the tunnel "battle front" the thunderous report from each dynamite blast was terrific, and the echoes would reverberate through the Big Creek Canyon, up and down, across and back, as though infuriated by the interference of the canyon walls. Zeus himself could not have done a better job.

The pistol drill was used, as compared to the present much-improved hammer type drill. A blacksmith shop stood at the mouth of each adit for the sharpening of the drill steel, which was done by hand. Today, most sharpening is done with a mechanical sharpener operated with compressed air. Instead of having storage battery or trolley locomotives for hauling out blasted rock or muck, we used mules. It was amazing to observe the intelligence of these animals. They would function almost automatically—about the only need for a driver was to see that they did not head for the stable during a trip outside, instead of returning for another load. The cars were loaded by hand, as the present day mechanical loaders had not yet been developed.

By keeping progress charts, it was easy to forecast the date when any two headings should break through. To be on hand for the final check in line and grade just after a break-through was an event in which our party was always keenly interested, since it would be the final test of the accuracy of our work. The closures were good, both in alignment and grade or elevation. When the checks were made, especially of alignment, it was always a favorite stunt of the fellow who had gone beyond the break-through to hold his pencil or plumb bob at least one foot off line. This gave the instrument man a shock, since he would not know whether or not his helper was holding the pencil on the proper point, and fearfully would signal him in the direction that coincided with the line carried forward. Finally, what a sigh of relief the instrument man gave when he learned that both lines came together on the lead pencil.

On my way through Fresno, enroute to Big Creek, I remained overnight at the Grand Central Hotel. It was extremely hot, and with many others I spent most of the night, until chased out by the "cops," in the Court House Park trying to keep cool. In checking out of the hotel the following morning, I arranged to have one large suit case kept in storage for about thirty days, leaving it on the floor in the lobby. Imagine my amazement when I returned one month later, after my first pay day, to be greeted by the suit case sitting in exactly the same spot where I had left it, intact in all respects, and well-blanketed with dust.

During my first travels over the job, I kept running across a most likable and busy little chap with rosy cheeks, who had a smile for everyone, and whom I took to be one of the "common herd" along with the rest of us. One day he asked if I were the fellow who had recently come down from Seattle, how I liked my job and if I were being treated all right. Finally, I asked him what he was doing, and it was then I learned he was Rex C. Starr, the ubiquitous assistant to the superintendent, Mr. Thebo. He appeared quite young to be holding such a responsible position, but I learned later that even though he had not been long away from his alma mater, he had been through a previous power development in the Pacific northwest.

Mr. Thebo and Mr. Starr were the kind of men the employees liked to see around, not the kind they would try to dodge—unless Starr was biting his finger nails. Then, look out!

Automobiles and trucks had not yet come into extensive use. Instead of these, there were many horses, mules and wagons—enough to have served adequately any of the large circuses.

There was only one automobile—a touring car—in the entire area. It was for the use of Mr. Thebo, and whenever a trip was contemplated to Huntington Lake, he would summon several men to accompany him to help push the car up the steep grades. Men soon learned to be unusually busy or hard to find whenever the car appeared in front of the superintendent's office.

One day I was asked to proceed to The Basin and check the alignment in Tunnel No. 1, about which there was some question. My party happened to be at Big Creek No. 2. At about two o'clock in the afternoon we picked up our paraphernalia and started to hike up the trail to West Portal, 2,000 feet in elevation and about two miles distant. Transportation was limited · in those days to "shanks' mare." I carried the heavy Berger transit, hoping we might be lucky enough to catch a ride from West Portal to Big Creek on "the peddler," the name applied to the engine serving the tunnel camps. No such luck—so we walked the five miles by railroad, and after a short rest started the six mile hike from Big Creek around the road to The Basin and Dam No 1. There was nothing in sight in the way of a team and wagon, even at Big Creek. We made Camp 1A just in time for supper, somewhat the worse for wear after the thirteen-mile hike and the four-thousand-foot climb. However, we felt better after our meal, and proceeded to check the underground tunnel

Beautiful Huntington Lake in the High Sierra of Central California is a popular summer resort as well as a source of water for power generation.

Engineers on the Big Creek project in 1913. R. C. Starr, arms folded, is standing next to F. M. Thebo, in center in open brown shirt.

*Above: General view of penstock No. 1
from top of Powerhouse No. 1.*

Left: Laying penstock No. 1 up 80% grade.

line, finishing the job in time for breakfast. The underground alignment was found to be considerably in error. (Today no one even thinks of going anywhere without using a car.)

Another job was to locate the set stakes for four cottages, which were the first permanent structures built. Although first occupied by Thebo, Starr, Shannon and Roberts, of the Stone & Webster staff, they eventually became the homes of operating employees. Little did I realize on that August day in 1912 that I would be concerned with these same houses in 1947.

The Basin, two thousand feet higher and directly above Big Creek, was the origin of a local witticism with respect to the Big Dipper as seen from Big Creek. One night an alert observer, recognizing the relation, wisecracked, "I see the Dipper is up in the Basin tonight." The name "Basin" was changed to Huntington Lake shortly after construction began, in honor of Henry E. Huntington —but it didn't really "take" until about 1914. When people become accustomed to a name, it is about as difficut to change it as changing a horse to a new stall.

A large construction job, especially one having prospects of continuing for some time, is always a good lure for the sprouting of various enterprises—some of them worthy—in the area. The names, Pressley, Alviso, Imhoff and Aggergaard are familiar to all oldtime Big Creekers as the forerunners of the few businesses remaining today. Big Creek's first store was built by Frank Alviso early in 1912, across the road from the present U. S. Forest Service garage. He sold out four years later to Imhoff and Aggergaard, the latter becoming sole owner in 1921. Aggergaard put up a new and larger store that year where Rasmussen's now stands. The former was destroyed by fire in the summer of 1930. Some competition appeared in 1916 when Pressley, an ex-conductor on the Southern Pacific, built a small store nearby, specializing in tobacco, punch boards and slot machines—also, in cashing checks. Big Creek stores, apparently, appealed to railroad conductors, as E. H. Barnett, formerly of the San Joaquin & Eastern, bought out Pressley and operated the place along with a string of pack stock. William Solomon came along, bought out Barnett, dismantled the building and built a new one, including a garage.

Mr. Thebo was anxious to have something better than bunkhouse quarters for guests. He encouraged A. O. Smith, of Clovis, to put up a hotel in 1913, adjacent to and just west of the present U. S. Forest Service garage. Later, several floored tents, or "rag houses," were erected opposite to handle the overflow. The hotel business was brisk enough by 1914 to encourage William Thrower, ex-forest ranger, to build his Big Creek Hotel near the present site occupied by the Forest Service gasoline pumps. Naturally, in those days such a building was on the rustic order, lacking many present day features—one being insulation against cold and noise. This was especially noticeable in the bathroom, which was separated from the main rooms by a thin, rough panel, affording one most extensive publicity; attending its use was a fearful sound that resembled that of the ice on the Yukon River breaking up in the spring. Thrower sold his hotel in 1920 to Ludwig Schurich, the owner of the present Big Creek Hotel. The former hotel was destroyed by fire in 1929.

Early in January, 1913, trouble developed in Camp No. 3, one of the tunnel camps and my headquarters. Men were complaining about the food. The climax was reached one night after supper when a group arrived at the mess hall carrying rope and with "blood in their eyes," allegedly to hang the cook. Word had gone ahead that such a move was under way, and as the advance guard went in the front door, the chef went out the back and disappeared. He never did return to that area. Coincident with the total tie-up set off by this outbreak, a heavy storm set in. The snow, four and five feet deep, would have made it impossible to continue effectively with the work for at least two weeks. The San Joaquin Light &

Power Corporation was furnishing power for the job, and the storm caused the failure of a half-mile span of the transmission line just outside headquarters camp, leaving the entire job without light and power. Even Dick Stout, chief electrician, was unable to restore service for two weeks. It was fortunate that the commissary and warehouse had a large supply of candles on hand.

When Austin Mason left in February, 1913, the assignment of tunnel engineer was given to me. I had been transit man and assistant engineer for some time. Banks had returned to the field laboratory to devote all his time to making and testing samples of cement and concrete, along with any other construction materials which might come his way. The greater part of the work went ahead on a seven day per week basis—some of it twenty-four hours a day.

Tunnel superintendent Criddle's transportation consisted of a horse and cart; Arthur Blight and I each had one of those three-wheeled contraptions called "speeders"—very nice to use on the downgrade, but not so pleasant to pump on the uphill return. Some thrill for us too, when we met the "peddler" on a sharp curve and had to yank the speeder off the track in a hurry—much to the amusement of the engine crew.

During the summer the job was again closed down for about a month, for recuperation from financial difficulties. Mr. Huntington came to the rescue, putting up his own collateral to insure completion of the work then under way.

There was not much in the way of special amusement in those days, and on Sundays those lucky enough to be off would head down the trail for Carlson's Hotel, now the location of Camp Sierra, for one of the chicken dinners made famous by Mrs. Carlson and her daughter, Pauline. The chicken would be piled so high in front of us, we had to "eat our way out"—not difficult to do even though it was flanked on all sides by Pauline's hot biscuits. Boy, how we did enjoy the change to a woman's cooking, and the "frills" not put out by the camp mess halls! Such "oases," including wonderful dinners from the hands of Mr. and Mrs. Banks, along with the most gracious hospitality, will never be forgotten.

As the result of the work my party had been doing—checking overhead and underground lines—it acquired the name of "pre-zacts," a combination of "precision" and "exact." Such work required the use of spring balances on the steel tape lines to insure equal tension in measuring distances. Corrections in steel tape measurements were made for temperatures either above or below the standard of 62°F. In later years accuracy was facilitated by the use of a steel tape calibrated in Washington, D. C., by the Bureau of Standards, and which was carefully guarded and used only when necessary for checking the tapes in daily use.

Provision for storage of water was necessary, and The Basin, at an elevation of seven thousand feet, filled this requirement. To make it into a reservoir, however, three large concrete dams had to be built. In addition to the three dams, the initial development included Power Houses 1 and 2, two tunnels—one four miles in length, the other three-quarters of a mile—one 84-inch flow line that was 6,600 feet long, four high pressure pipe lines, or penstocks, each about one mile in length, and a double transmission line two hundred and forty-eight miles long to operate at the highest voltage —150,000 volts—ever used commercially. An early start on such construction was vital because the schedule called for the first power house and one transmission line to Los Angeles to go into service July 1, 1913, followed by the second plant and line by October 1. With such objectives it was necessary that the reservoir be ready to impound water from the 1913 spring run-off; otherwise, there would be one year's loss of water and, naturally, the same delay in time. In all such mountain power systems, the water is gone until the following year if it is not retained as the snow melts in the spring.

Camps, of course, had be be established for all such operations, and Camp 2, the headquarters, was already flourishing. The plans provided that the camps to serve the two areas accommodate a total of two thousand men. Camp 1, in the bottom of the reservoir area about three-quarters of a mile northeast of Dam 1, was the location from which all gravel was obtained for the concrete going into the dams and pertinent structures. The alphabet was used extensively to identify other camps in the area. Camp 1A served principally during the construction of Dam No. 1. 1B took care of Tunnel No. 1. 1C, located where Huntington Lodge now stands, cared for those working on Dam No. 2. 1D, somewhat down the canyon, was the base for the installation of the 84-inch flow line, and the men engaged in building Dam 3 lived in Camp 1E. So many camps, instead of one central location, were justified because a camp near the job had advantages over distant quarters. The area involved was so large that, to serve the various sites, thirteen miles of standard gauge construction railroad had to be built, and nine locomotives, together with over a hundred standard railroad freight cars, were provided. The greater portion of such equipment was used in the Huntington Lake area, all of it being moved up the incline cable-way. A second incline was constructed from West Portal on the San Joaquin & Eastern Railroad to Power House No. 2. Both inclines were a little over a mile long, rising about two thousand feet, with the maximum grade about eighty per cent—a rise of eighty feet vertically in one hundred feet horizontally. The incline cars were standard railroad flats with a "strong back" on the lower end to prevent loads from sliding, and were kept in service permanently. Thousands of tons of material, equipment and supplies were handled without serious mishaps.

Clearing and excavation at the sites of the three dams started during the summer of 1912, as did the driving of Tunnel No. 1.

Compared to present day equipment, the guy derricks and skips used in excavation for the dams were slow but sure. The pouring of concrete for Dams 1 and 2 continued through the winter, even though low temperatures prevailed. Steam pipes under canvas were the protective measures used to prevent freezing. Dams 1 and 2 were completed shortly after the first of the year 1913, leaving Dam 3, the smallest one, trailing behind because trouble was experienced in excavation. Bed rock was deep, and much more difficult to reach than the foundation for either of the other two dams. The three sluice gates in the bottom of Dam No. 1 were closed for the first time on April 8, 1913, causing Big Creek to halt abruptly, accustomed as it had been to cascading down the canyon since time immemorial. Such was the beginning of the reservoir to be known later as Huntington Lake.

The reservoir area was, quite naturally, largely covered with trees, many of which were cut from a boat, as the water rose at the time of the first filling. Such a method explains why stumps are as much as twenty feet in height when water is at low stage. There was no time to dispose of the trees after they were cut, and they remained where they fell. This was a serious mistake, as we found in later years. Today government regulations demand a good clean-up of such areas, and any power company would not want it otherwise—not only from the standpoint of good house-keeping but also because of relief from subsequent trouble caused by floating debris. In later years, large expenditures have been made to remove many of these "sinkers," which usually float large end up and become a general nuisance, to say nothing of being unsightly.

Literally, the woods were full of engineers, or "S.I.'s," as they are called in construction vernacular—from the first letters of the legendary backwoods spelling "Sivil Injuneer."

The engineers' quarters at The Basin were located on the spot now occupied by Huntington Lake Lodge. Several of the men made pets of chipmunks, which are numerous in these parts. A large enclosure was made with suitable wire netting, adjacent to the building, and boxes were arranged with material for nests. The little fellows were easy to tame, and afforded no end of amusement during the long winter evenings with their antics. Small holes were cut in the partition between the pen and the main room of the building. It was amusing to watch them enter through these holes, scamper around the room, and end up in various pockets looking for peanuts, of which they were very fond, and of which they usually found plenty. Let a stranger enter, and they would scatter in all directions, resulting in a traffic jam at each exit. Soon a head would reappear at each hole, and before long all would venture in again. If the stranger sized up to their satisfaction, all well and good, but if he made any suspicious moves or gestures, the mad scamper would be on again. Once a workman who was going home for a few days to Los Angeles took a dozen chipmunks to his children— or at least started out with that number. He made the trip by train. The little pets-to-be were carried in a suitable ventilated box; everything was lovely. The workman stopped at one of the large stores in downtown Los Angeles to make some purchases for the family. Somehow the cage was accidentally knocked off the counter. The lid came off, releasing the occupants, and they scattered throughout the place. With much effort on the part of many employees, a few of the chipmunks were found that day—one being discovered in the pocket of a new overcoat. The manager, naturally, was deeply concerned over possible damage to goods and assigned special help to round up the little fellows. It was several days, even with the help of some of the members of the fire department, before a full accounting could be made—allowing everybody to rest more easily.

The concrete foundation for Big Creek Power House No. 1 was poured during March, 1913, followed in April by the one for Big Creek No. 2. The work on both plants was progressing satisfactorily, and No. 1 was completed, when No. 2 met with disaster. Just as the roof was finished, and before the concrete had a chance to set, fire broke out in the adjacent carpenter shop and spread to the concrete forms, enveloping the entire structure. Consequently, the huge roof fell upon the upper floors, causing major damage. The extensive repairs delayed the plant's going into service until December 18, 1913. Although Plant No. 1 did not go into regular service until November 10, when the transmission line was completed, it had been delivering power to local circuits since October 14.

The initial development utilized the water from Huntington Lake through a total fall of nearly four thousand feet. Subsequent development increased the fall to upwards of six thousand feet. It may be of interest to see how the water performs. Let us follow its course from the reservoir through screens, or rack bars, into the large intake tower, thence through the twelve-foot tunnel, three-quarters of a mile long. The screens, which are necessary and common for all such structures, prevent the passage of moving debris. Connecting with the tunnel today are two pipes of 84-inch and 60-inch diameter, called flow lines, which are each a little over one mile in length. The high pressure pipe lines, or penstocks, are connected to the lower end of the flow lines, and extend down the steep mountainside to Power House No. 1. They terminate at the power house in eight nozzles, each six inches in diameter, one for each water wheel, and two water wheels for each unit, from which the water discharges at a velocity of about three hundred and fifty feet per second. These jets, almost like bars of steel, discharge across an open space of a few inches to strike the buckets of the water wheels. A tremendous impact might be expected, but the shock is relieved since the part of the bucket, when first touched, is nearly parallel to the jet. The water's course over the surface of the buckets is momentary, and without much pressure and velocity it falls into the tailrace. For the drop of 2,100 feet, the pressure at the water wheels is between 900 and 1,000 pounds per square inch. The control of pressure and the economical use of water at varying loads is provided for, each wheel having a governor, so that maximum efficiency can be obtained from a unit by using one or both wheels according to load demand.

The size of the jet, or the amount of water being discharged, is regulated by a needle valve controlled by the governor, and excessive changes in pipe line pressures are relieved by bypass openings back of the nozzles, also controlled by the governor. After reaching the tailrace, the water, instead of continuing unchecked down the natural canyon, must repeat its first performance because its job is only half done—and is again impounded, this time by Dam 4 across Big Creek just below Power House No. 1. The water passes through a four-mile tunnel and into the high pressure lines, through which it is carried to work on the wheels in Power House No. 2.

The high pressure pipe for the four units installed during the initial development—two in each of the two plants—was made in Germany. When it was laid, the work was started at the power house and the sections placed up-hill, the lines being kept full of water as they grew in length. The water allowed a lower and more even temperature to be maintained, and in warm weather would hold the pipe movement in the trench to a minimum. It is amazing how pipe lines will react to temperature changes—crawling around like snakes if care is not taken. The practice of providing expansion joints was adopted in later years, but since there are none in these older lines they were back-filled, that is, covered with earth. The lap-welding process for making the longitudinal seams had been developed and used extensively in Germany in the manufacture of pipe for such purposes. Two Germans were sent here by the factory, to remain during the installation of its product, to represent the manufacturer and be of possible assistance in laying the pipe. Those of us on the job did not realize there was any great difference in rank between the two until our attention was directed to the situation quite forcibly. Some reference was made to Katagan about his partner, Kawalski, whereupon Katagan retorted indignantly, "He iss not my partner—he iss my man."

Mr. Shuffleton, western manager for Stone & Webster, was in general charge of the initial development. Although he did not spend much time here, he made frequent visits to keep in close touch with the progress. A self-made man, he was second to none when it came to handling difficult construction, no matter how large or complicated. If there were a pumping problem—and most construction jobs have many—one was sure to find him there. He had a way with pumps, particularly second-hand ones, and after getting them on the job he certainly could make the "darn" things perform wonders. It mattered not how wet, muddy, or otherwise disagreeable a location for a pump might be, he would be found there, covered with mud and grease from his black derby to his feet. He never bothered about coveralls—staying with it until the pump was working to his satisfaction. Scornful of slide rules, he had his own methods, and quite frequently would quickly correct, through his mental processes, a fellow using a "guessing stick."

He was disdainful of carrying luggage, and took long trips without so much as a hand bag. The only time I ever saw him with any kind of a bag was once in Fresno. He apologized for the luggage, explaining that Mrs. Shuffleton was along.

Visitors to this project have been legion, and I can truthfully say that of them all, Mr. Shuffleton was outstanding. During a visit here several years ago, he was, as usual, most entertaining in every way and keenly interested in everything, no matter what nor how small. During this trip he remarked to Mrs. Redinger that he had been too busy for many years to bother with vacations, whereupon she inquired how he managed to get married. He explained it occurred when there was a lull in construction and he was not very busy for a few days. Unfortunately, I have never obtained Mrs. Shuffleton's version.

Late in November, 1913, while I was temporarily stationed in a camp at Indian Mission checking over a trunk telephone line, I received a message from Big Creek headquarters that, along with hundreds of other men, I was being laid off, the initial development by Stone & Webster having reached completion except for final clean-up.

At 1:15 a.m., December 1, 1913, the first penstock failure occurred when a flanged joint pulled apart in the right-hand leg of Line No. 2, Big Creek No. 1, just above the public highway. The weather was cold and the heavy spray, spreading completely over the nearby steel transmission tower, froze, causing it to collapse. The power house was flooded, not only with water but also sand and mud—and, of course, was put out of commission. Steam pumps were rushed into service to help clear the basement. The San Joaquin Light & Power Corporation came to the rescue with power for light circuits and crane operation during the emergency.

At completion of the initial development, this plant had the highest head in this country. The word "head" is used in hydraulics to designate the vertical distance between reservoir level and the water wheels. The water wheels and the generators were the largest of their type built up to that time.

Some idea may be had of the growing demand for power in the territory served then, by the fact that when construction began it was planned to provide 40,000 kilowatts of capacity. The plan had to be revised and the plants built to deliver 60,000 kilowatts from the substation, with liberal provisions throughout for increases in capacity. To provide for future demands, the transmission lines were built for three times the capacity first contemplated. About this same time a large proportion, 78% of the company's power sold, was used by electric railways—the Los Angeles Railway operating 355 miles, and the Pacific Electric 868 miles of interurban lines in Southern California.

In the extent and value of its properties in 1914, together with its volume of sales, the Pacific Light & Power Corporation ranked as one of the largest and most successful public utilities on the Pacific Coast.

V

Intermission—World War 1

A S SOON AS THE first development was completed, the Stone & Webster forces moved out. In one respect, any construction job is like a large circus—even including the clowns. As soon as the "show" is over, the outfit moves elsewhere. Rex Starr became affiliated with the Pacific Light & Power Corporation as hydraulic engineer, with Arthur Blight as assistant. Hundreds of others scattered to the four winds. After the exodus, there was a lull in the area with respect to major construction, but not with the two large power houses just completed, as they settled down to grinding out kilowatts for rapidly growing Southern California, the job for which they were built.

On the door of one of the many offices in the newly-built Marsh-Strong Building in Los Angeles, later renamed Rives-Strong, appeared the sign, "Banks & Redinger"—who were to take on various and sundry jobs of an engineering nature. We realized we had to seek new affiliations, and were of the opinion that while doing so, it would be desirable to have some spot to which we could return to "rest our legs." If, in the meantime, the sign should attract something, all well and good. Apparently we did not use the right kind of "fly paper," because nothing of consequence came our way, although we did have a few nibbles and much fun out of the venture for a while. Then the situation took on a different color since office rent was not being donated and we had to live.

Banks and I were resting our "dogs" in the office one day, planning some more moves, when our 'phone (yes, we had one) rang. Both jumped as if it were a fire alarm. Starr was calling for Redinger, and wanted to know if he would be interested in a job. We had to present a good front, of course—or at least we thought we did—and indicated that we had several very good prospects at the moment, but that we would be glad to listen to any proposition, while at the same time being careful not to be "dropped off the hook." He was given time, with some difficulty, to hang up his receiver before I rushed into his office. The firm of Banks & Redinger dissolved shortly, both individuals going to work for the Pacific Light & Power Corporation—and what a sigh of relief we gave. Starr sent me to the Redondo Steam Plant to do what was necessary to reinforce the pier supporting the large pipe lines which carried the condensing water from the ocean to the boilers, as an unusually heavy sea was threatening serious damage. This assignment was cut short when a United States marshal suddenly appeared with a subpoena requiring my appearance in Seattle immediately, in connection with the Alaska coal land investigation on which I had been engaged before coming to Big Creek.

Upon my return to Los Angeles several weeks later, Starr took me to the Azusa power house, now owned by Pasadena, to make some tunnel repairs. A bad cave-in had occurred between the intake and the power house, causing a complete shut-down. After finishing this, I returned to Big Creek, located the intake portal of the tunnel to be driven between Power Houses 2 and 3 (the latter not yet built); also the outlet portal of the tunnel headed for Mammoth Pool on the San Joaquin River. Although both tunnels were started shortly thereafter—it was now June, 1914, a slow schedule was adopted and followed until there was a change in plans at the time of an urgent need for additional power, resulting in the birth of Power House No. 8.

Having located these portals, along with the first tangent of both tunnels, my party was preparing to move to headquarters when we heard about the forthcoming arrival in Big Creek of a large group of girls from the Fresno State Normal School. One can hardly imagine the excitement which resulted among the few engineers left at that time. It certainly put us on the *que vive*. Fifty young women arrived on July 3, having enrolled in what was to become one of the major enterprises in this area, the Summer School of the Fresno institution. The Fresno State Normal School had been established in 1911 and was renamed "Fresno Teachers College" in 1921. By an act of the State Legislature the present name, "Fresno State College," was adopted in 1935.

The quarters occupied at Big Creek for that first summer session consisted of several of the rough buildings such as bunk-houses and mess hall remaining from the 1912-1913 construction. Such primitive accommodations did not encourage continuation of the project, but because of the Pan-Pacific International Exposition in San Francisco in 1915 there were no classes that year. By 1916 a site had been selected at Huntington Lake near the Huntington Lake Lodge, which had been built in the meantime, where the school flourished each summer until 1926, when it moved to a permanent base—a forty-acre tract adjacent to Lakeshore on the north side of the Lake. At that location the school has continued each season with an enrollment of 250 to 350, until war conditions prevented its operation in 1943, 1944 and 1945. The sessions have always been very popular in such environment, since the students are able to enjoy unusual recreation while making professional progress. The Black-Foxe Military School of Los Angeles occupied for several years the site relinquished by the summer school near Huntington Lake Lodge.

It was amazing how much work we suddenly found close to headquarters after arrival of the summer school group, but our plans were quickly frustrated when we learned we were to leave Huntington Lake early on July 5 for reconnaissance along the upper South Fork of the San Joaquin River, twenty-five to forty miles distant by trail. This sudden change in plans did not interfere with our attending the dance at Big Creek the evening before—even though we knew we would have to hike to Huntington Lake afterwards in the wee small hours of the morning. We reached the engineers' quarters at Huntington Lake about four o'clock—allowing us about an hour before we would have to get breakfast and have our bedrolls ready to turn over to the packers by six o'clock. We did not think it worth while undressing, let alone opening our bedrolls, and scattered throughout the large room upstairs looking for a place to "flop." Suddenly it occurred to me that I might sneak into the only room in one corner of the spacious upstairs and "sleep soft." The room had been made, furnished and set aside for the use of the "brass hats," and usually the door was kept locked when unoccupied. I thought perhaps someone might have failed to lock it, and no one else in our group would think of making any investigation. There had been no "brass hats" around during the day, so to the room I went, feeling my way and being careful not to fall over anyone stretched out on the floor. The door was unlocked, and "what luck!"—so I thought. I opened it carefully, stepped inside, and closed it so quietly a mouse would not have been disturbed. I sat down on the bed, removed my shoes and started to undress, when there was a woman's voice, "What's going on here?" I didn't know one of the engineers had brought his wife along. Out the door I went, without my shoes, and as for sleep the next hour, I had none. It was not altogether the shock, but the only suitable spot I could find to lie down on quickly was on some cold folded canvas, part of our camp equipment going out with us that day.

There were two parties—one headed by H. L. Wheeler, the other by me—all men hiking except the packers. Saddle horses for such a group were not provided in those days, and if they had been offered we would have been very much surprised, if not offended.

The trip to Blaney Meadows, via Red Mountain and Hot Springs Pass, was broken by camping overnight on the way. Wheeler started his work on the right hand side of the South Fork of the San Joaquin River, heading upstream, and I began on the other. A line of levels was carried all the way from Huntington Lake to Piute and Evolution Creeks. This was to determine the elevation above sea level of all important points of our work. We were investigating the feasibility of carrying water from the higher elevations across Hot Springs Pass and into the Huntington Lake watershed. We thought nothing of climbing as much as two thousand feet each morning to our work, and over terrain as rough as one could find. I recall one experience while we were running our line around and far up on the side of the Pavilion Dome, a steep cliff. Hand and toe holds along the sheer face were scant, but we had become adept in the use of "skyhooks" under such conditions. I got into a spot from which I could not extricate myself without leaving my six foot steel rod, which a chief of party carries when he goes ahead to assist in running a survey line. The rod, no doubt, is still there, as no one but an alpine climber would ever attempt to scale such a cliff just for fun.

Blaine Riley, transit man, had a narrow escape when he slipped, but fortunately he was able to catch a hand-hold by letting loose of the Berger transit. A sheer drop of at least a thousand feet was below him.

A good idea of the terrain may be had by my saying that one day's run covered a total distance of only one hundred yards. Our line was carried along on contour, and it was not unusual to look down on our camp, one to two thousand feet below. The camp was moved frequently enough to make our trips as short as possible horizontally, but nothing much could be done about the vertical distances.

We were surprised and annoyed one morning upon arriving at the place on line where we had left our transit, tapes, axes, etc. the evening before, to find that during the night the string from our plumb bobs and the buttons from our coats and jackets had been eaten off and carried away. The transit could not be accurately set, of course, without a plumb bob, but we worried along through the day, since a round trip to camp for anyone would have taken several hours. We profited from this lesson about chipmunks.

For pastime on Sunday, if we did not work, we would usually take a "postman's holiday"—go on a hike and climb some mountain peak, the highest in the vicinity. Being so near, we couldn't pass up a visit to Evolution Lake, and several were unable to resist the temptation to climb Mt. Darwin, in spite of its elevation—almost 14,000 feet. The naming of the lake and mountain is credited to Theodore S. Solomons, in 1895. It is only natural for one to call to mind the Darwinian theory when confronted with the names of the above lake and mountain, and those on government maps—Wallace, Spencer, Fiske and Haeckel—all close High Sierra neighbors and often referred to as "The Evolution Group of Philosophers."

The names or initials, with dates, carved on quaking aspens along the trails, attest to the fact our party went that way, but we were by no means the first, as we saw date scars of the 1870's.

At the outbreak of World War I our camp was located far up on Evolution Creek. "Sippi" Johnson, from headquarters, had ridden through the night and most of the day, bringing instructions to "button up" the job and return to Big Creek.

The next morning, August 20, we were up before daylight, and believe me, that was early. Our bedrolls were quickly made ready for the packers, and after a hasty breakfast we headed for Big Creek on foot, some thirty-five or forty trail miles via Blaney Meadows and Hot Springs Pass—all acting like a bunch of pack mules and saddle horses making for the corral after having been turned loose. Being in perfect trim for such a hike, we did not stop long enough for our light lunch, preferring to eat it on the fly, and literally slid down Pitman Creek into Big Creek. Our arrival was marred only by our method of entering camp. It was twilight, and to minimize embarrassment in case we should meet any women, we entered headquarters by a circuitous route. Even with such precautions we walked circumspectly at times, as the seats of our pants had been completely worn away by sliding over rocks.

On the trail we wondered whether any of the summer school girls might have remained at Big Creek, but concluded such a prospect was hopeless, since we knew the summer session was scheduled to end August 15. We were delighted to find a few of those we had met on July 3 remaining over for a period of rest and relaxation, which was cut short by our arrival. The girls seemed not to object, and proceeded to entertain us royally with wonderful breakfasts and dinners, prepared and served in one of the old bunkhouses.

It should not be difficult for anyone to understand how ten days of such treatment affected us, after having had no meals prepared by such lovely hands for nearly two months. It was the forerunner of "disastrous" results for one member of the Fresno State College group who was the head of the Home Economics Department—because about three years later, and after much persuasion, she became Mrs. Redinger.

As a result of World War I, the Company stopped all field work such as that which we had been doing, and again, along with the other members of both survey parties, I found myself laid off as of September 1, 1914.

Lobby of Huntington Lake Lodge in 1926.

Huntington Lake Lodge in later years. It was to be torn down in 1949.

The author, David H. Redinger, in front of Powerhouse No. 1 in 1947.

VI

We Winter in Arizona

THOSE OF US WHO had been turned loose were again in the market for a job. We wondered where we would find one, in view of our type of work being curtailed wherever possible on account of the European situation. We scattered in all directions. I found myself in San Francisco, where, coincidentally, I had been called by the United States Land Office to appear at another hearing in connection with the Alaska coal lands case. It was not long before several of the Big Creekers, including "Hank" Wheeler, the late O. J. Schieber, and I, thanks to "Ollie," were enjoying the "nosebags" of the U. S. Reclamation Service on the Salt River Valley Project at Phoenix, Arizona.

Naturally, the work involved irrigation problems, and for some time my party was located at Mesa, where we occupied a tent without a floor, in the U. S. Reclamation Service's mule corral— no foolin'—but the mules were nice and as gentle as mules know how to be. Two of them pulled us around in a regulation line wagon, and naturally we became quite well acquainted—so much so, that they thought they should sleep with us in our crowded tent.

Walter Jessup (today the Western representative of the American Society of Civil Engineers) had a deluxe tent, floored and screened, with even a kerosene heater, in a somewhat more secluded section of the corral than ours. Frequently, when it was unoccupied, we would take advantage, slip in and spend an enjoyable night amid such luxuries.

43

Some of the area we covered is today occupied either by a dude ranch or a swank hotel, such as the Arizona Biltmore and Camel Back Inn.

How well I recall being one of the thousands on hand to greet Barney Oldfield, that day in 1915, as he finished the historic non-stop run from Los Angeles to Phoenix. He was easy to recognize because of the ever-present cigar, and I can still see him and his mechanic as they roared through the outskirts of Phoenix while the tumultous roadside throngs waved frantically and got spattered with mud, much of which the car threw at least fifty feet in the air. Besides affording the populace immense thrills, such endurance runs had much to do with the development of the automobile.

One Sunday morning, in Phoenix, while walking to breakfast, I observed a heavy pall of black smoke. My favorite eating place, Gass Brothers Cafe, was engulfed in flames, and along with it was my weekly meal ticket purchased the night before. As was customary, I had left it with the cashier. As I did not have any change it was necessary to rouse some friends out of bed and "interview" them before I could eat.

Not long after this incident, I was on my way to the bank where I had recently deposited my limited funds. It was not smoke this time, but a large crowd in the street. There was a sign on the door—yes, you guessed it—announcing that the bank had failed. Again friends had to come to my rescue. Like the meal ticket, this loss was never recovered.

It afforded me pleasure, while in Arizona, to make preliminary arrangements on the ground for the monument which now stands near the El Tovar Hotel at the Grand Canyon, in honor of Major Powell, reported to be the first white man to make the hazardous trip down the Colorado River.

Phoenix, no doubt, will long remember New Year's Eve, 1915,

when prohibition went into effect. All wet goods not consumed before midnight were carried away by the bottle, case, armful— any method available. I saw one man pushing a wheelbarrow down the street—full to the brim, like himself. Fixtures were yanked from their moorings, hauled, and even manhandled, through the streets—the all-night spirit being that of one huge carnival instead of a "swan song."

I have always been thankful for the Arizona experience, because I learned not only to like the desert, the giant Saguaro cactus, the horned toads, but also to appreciate fully the meaning of "the desert in bloom."

The Arizona assignment, coupled with three months in the employ of the California Highway Commission at San Luis Obispo and Bradley, constituted a period long enough to cause a break in continuity of service with the Pacific Light & Power Corporation, and the loss of three and a half preceding years.

VII

Huntington Lake Lodge

As there was no hotel above Big Creek, the officials of the
Pacific Light & Power Corporation became deeply interested in such a venture. After due consideration they
reached a decision to build one at Huntington Lake. Such an undertaking appeared to have promise—especially in a mountain setting
at an elevation of seven thousand feet, and with the railroad to
serve the hotel. The Huntington Lake Hotel Company was formed
as a subsidiary of the Pacific Light & Power Corporation, and the
site selected was one beneath the pines on the south shore near the
west end of the lake, readily accessible by road.

Huntington Lake Lodge was completed early enough in 1915
to allow it to be opened on July 4. H. M. Nickerson, who was
associated with the Huntington Hotel in Pasadena, was engaged
to supervise construction and to manage the hotel after it was
opened. He returned for the 1916 season but had to relinquish
management early because of illness. Mr. Huntington arranged
for the services of Howard B. Brown, who headed the staff of
Mt. Lowe Hotel, and he completed the season. Carl A. Babb, who
had operated the Shasta Springs Hotel, became manager beginning
with the 1917 season, and served through 1925. He was followed
by Fred Williams, formerly of the Hughes Hotel in Fresno, who
carried on from 1926 to 1931.

Considerable enthusiasm was shown for snow sports during
the first winter after the lodge was opened. The Commercial Club

of Fresno—sixty-five members strong—constituted the party making up the first "Ice and Snow Carnival," as it was called. The success of that outing is nicely described by George Wharton James, of Pasadena, in his booklet, "Winter Sports at Huntington Lake Lodge," dated Cascada, February 22, 1916. To my knowledge, that was the only such outing ever held in winter during the life of the lodge. The principal barrier to winter sports in the area, as far as the lodge was concerned, was the problem of keeping open the road between Big Creek and Huntington Lake under winter conditions. Justification for such heavy expense, along with that for operating the lodge, would have required patronage larger than could have been expected in those days. For about the first ten years of operation, most of the guests came by train to Big Creek, where they were met and driven by bus up the two-thousand-foot climb.

Naturally, the seasons were short, and although the hotel would open about June 1, guests would be few until the middle of that month unless the weather was unusually good. By the middle of September the lodge would close. It became a natural center for activities at the lake, continuing as such through the early '20's.

The road around the north shore to the upper end of the lake was constructed in 1920 by the United States Bureau of Public Roads, the Isabella Construction Company being the contractor. The completion of this road really marked the beginning of what has become a large and popular summer resort, to the extent of about four hundred individually-owned cottages, several stores, hotel accommodations, Forest Service camp grounds, various schools and three post offices. On the south shore, but not accessible by road, Boy Scout camps have been established, and one large deluxe camp for boys. Prior to the construction of the road along the north shore, a few cabins were built, the material being ferried across the lake in row boats. The first one built was intended for

Henry E. Huntington, but he never saw it. Later the grounds were used by the lodge for entertaining its guests with barbecues and wienie roasts. The trips made across the lake to the camps on moonlight nights were picturesque and delightful. To add to the enjoyment, the boat usually towed a barge large enough to permit dancing. Long to be remembered is the full moon rising, especially on the nights, usually in August, when it appears to be pushing itself out of the very top of distant Red Mountain. This is a magnificent sight when seen from anywhere, and especially so if viewed from the northwesterly shores of the lake. The moon moves to the north each night, of course, and when it comes over the mountain on the south shore of the lake, the pine trees at the top are so clearly silhouetted that one can almost see the chipmunks running along the limbs—except that they know better than to be out at that time of night.

Guests were always cautioned, when they went hiking or horseback riding, to stay on the well-blazed trails so as to take no chance of getting lost. If they insisted on going, and were not sure of themselves, they would be offered a guide to accompany them. On one occasion a woman guest was anxious to take a ride over some of the trails but did not want to be bothered with anyone accompanying her, insisting that she knew how to handle herself adequately in the mountains. Off she went—on the back of one of the best mountain horses the lodge owned. She became confused in the vicinity of Black Point. After losing the trail, and instead of allowing the horse free rein—he would have brought her back—she tied him to a tree, saddled and bridled, and started hiking. She was out overnight and said she had spent it sitting in a tree, since she was afraid of wild animals. Later in the day she appeared at one of our lower power houses, several mountain miles below, much bedraggled and exhausted. No one knew until then what direction to start on a search for the horse. He was found on the third day—the poor fellow still tied to the tree and ready for water and barley.

The lodge was the scene of many capacity gatherings, some sponsored by the Edison Company, and others, particularly conventions, on their own. It seemed to be a favorite spot for newspaper men to hold forth. Registered were many interesting guests, both local and from various parts of our own as well as foreign countries. One meeting I remember quite distinctly. The day after a convention of Pacific Coast lumber men, I was having dinner in the lodge dining room, when Manager Babb told me a gentleman was waiting in the lobby and was quite anxious to see me. He gave his name as "MacGregor," representing himself as being on the staff of the *Edinburgh Scotsman*. He wanted to learn all he could about the "wonderful power development then in progress in these parts," as he wished to give the story to his paper for the information of its readers throughout England and Scotland. He reported loss of his wallet on the train from Fresno that afternoon. Besides losing all the cash he had, he appeared to be more worried about the loss of his passport. I would have been apprehensive had it not been for presentation of a card bearing the name of a highly respected gentleman who had been in attendance at the.lumbermen's convention the day before. The editor of *The Timberman* (Portland) had written a friendly introduction to me on his card, so all was taken to be in order. In those days, many men were being transported by train daily to the job, and steps were taken immediately to post notices in all camps, offering a reward for the return of the passport. No information was forthcoming. In the meantime, Manager Babb was asked to take care of MacGregor as a company guest.

Several days later, MacGregor was invited to my office, where he met George C. Ward, then vice-president in charge of all construction. MacGregor made an appointment with him that evening, and I was present. Mr. Ward took the time to give MacGregor quite a comprehensive story in considerable detail—in fact, enough to fill two stenographer's notebooks. Whether any of the notes he was making could be deciphered afterwards became questionable shortly to both of us. The morning after the interview, MacGregor came back to my office. More than a week had now elapsed, and not having heard anything about his allegedly lost wallet, he indicated his anxiety to reach the British Consul in San Francisco, pointing out that he could not accomplish much about a passport by wire. In Mr. Ward's presence, I asked MacGregor how much money he felt he would need to get to San Francisco and see him through until he could get his affairs in shape. The sum of $125.00 appeared to him to be sufficient. With Mr. Ward's approval, (he had indicated on the side that he thought we should help the fellow) that amount was given him from our local funds. He departed, to contact the British Consul and make necessary arrangements by cable to replace his passport and to secure additional funds.

Not having heard from MacGregor after two weeks, we sent a letter of inquiry to the editor of *The Timberman,* in Portland, since his card had been used as MacGregor's introduction. The reply stated he had met MacGregor in Fresno upon the former's return from the convention at the Lodge. After being told by MacGregor that he was on the staff of a paper, and was also a fellow countryman, the editor suggested he go to Big Creek and write up the project for the *Scotsman.* Feeling his responsibility for Mac-Gregor's Big Creek trip, the editor cabled the *Edinburgh Scotsman.* No such person was known by any member of its staff. To add insult to injury, MacGregor, upon reaching Fresno the evening of the day on which he left Big Creek, met by chance a very good friend of mine in the Hotel Fresno. He convinced my friend that he, MacGregor, was also a very close friend of mine. As the result of his super-salesmanship, he obtained the loan of my friend's overcoat for use in San Francisco until he could buy one. Needless to say, the Edison Company remains $125.00 in the red, plus expenses at the lodge, and my Fresno friend was the one who had to buy the new overcoat.

After sixteen years of operation, the lodge closed at the end of the 1931 season, since which time it has served for three short periods to house construction crews, as well as the State Guard, on duty in this area during World War II.

VIII

We Rebuild a Large Flume

ON MARCH 11, 1916, I returned to the Pacific Light & Power Corporation as engineer for the summer, on the reconstruction of the Borel Flume where it crosses Kern River at Isabella. The conduit of which this flume is a part carries water to the Borel Power House from the Kern River, the intake being at Kernville. Six months were required for building the high concrete piers in the river bed and for replacing the timber substructure of the large flume to be supported by these piers. The field work was done under the supervision of Bill Whitmire. The heavy bridge timbers and the cement were freighted by wagon from Caliente, the nearest railroad station, forty miles distant, over the old Walker Basin Road via Havilah. The present river road was not built until later years.

Common to almost all construction jobs are the words, "time is of the essence," and the one at Isabella was no exception. In order to have some relaxation and fun, we worked longer than our regular ten hour shifts, thereby gaining enough time to allow us to take every other Sunday for a fishing trip. Several of the men had their families at Isabella for the summer. On the evening before the Sunday off, the wives would have prepared such items of food as are usually taken on a camping trip, but in quantity sufficient, one thought, to last for a week instead of over one night. Occasionally, there was a huge wash tub filled with fried chicken. The large lumber wagon, piled high with bedding, eats and men, would leave ahead of Whitmire, who brought up the rear in his Model "T", loaded inside and out with women and children. Even the husky mules appeared to be just as anxious to get to Erskine Creek or Bull Run, where fishing was really good in those days. There must be something wrong with a man who does not enjoy some good companions, a camp fire, the food cooked over it—especially coffee made in a gallon tomato can—and the prospects of snagging some wary trout on the morrow.

On one of our outings we came up rather shy on fried chicken. "Sippi" Johnson and I were delegated to go through the country and find the fryers (he always called them "gumps") for one outing. As we were returning to camp from a ranch near Weldon, the jolting wagon shook the crate open. The chickens scattered in all directions, and only one of us could enter in the chase because the other had to stay with the mules, there being no place to tie them. I could not run fast enough, and we returned to camp after dark with only a half dozen.

One day we received a report about a failure of the 84-inch steel flow line at Huntington Lake. Shortly after midnight on the morning of May 14, a circumferential joint pulled apart, the rivets having sheared because of the enormous side pressure of a slide from above. The entire hillside, saturated from the melting snow, had decided to move, and would not be thwarted by a mere man-made pipe line, even though it was large. It is strange how many major failures of various kinds occur at the most inconvenient hours. The damaged line was the only one at that time carrying water from Huntington Lake to the penstocks feeding Power House No. 1. Consequently, that plant was out of service until May 17 while repairs were being made. Steps had to be taken for harnessing the hillside permanently in case it should continue to be temperamental, because enforced outages of the plants below are serious. The present huge concrete structure, deeply and securely anchored, enclosing the large pipe line through the dangerous area, was built that summer. The design allows a slide to slip over the roof and down the canyon without disturbing the pipe in case the hillside should take another notion to "go places."

As the summer progressed, we learned of the proposed work for increasing the height of the Huntington Lake dams. It appeared probable that we would move to that location with the completion of the flume repairs in September.

Wooden trestle carried water of Borel flume across Kern River. Pictured here as it was in 1918, trestle was later replaced with more modern structure.

Dam 1 at Huntington Lake in 1928 before it was backfilled on down-stream side. Intake tower at upper left.

Dam 3 at Huntington Lake in 1935.

IX

Raising Huntington Lake Dams

THE USE OF ELECTRICITY was increasing rapidly, and to meet the load demands, additional water for power had to be provided. The decision was made to enlarge Huntington Lake by increasing the height of the three dams by thirty-five feet, this being in accord with the United States Government permit under which the project was being developed. The storage capacity would be increased to almost 89,000 acre feet.

To insure such a major job being completed the following year— it was now early in 1916—everything had to be in readiness to proceed as early as spring conditions would allow. Final approval was given to start as of September 1, and immediately everything was shifted into high gear. A huge supply of lumber had to be provided, and quickly, as camps had to be built, the saw-mill reconditioned, a large rock crushing plant constructed, power lines extended, railroad tracks laid, air compressors installed, cement stored, and material of many kinds obtained.

The responsibility for the job in the field was given to Rex Starr, who brought Bill Whitmire from Isabella as general foreman. I came along as resident engineer. Hospital facilities were one of the first things to be provided, under Dr. O. I. Bemis, and were established at old Camp 1-D below Huntington Lake Lodge, at the same location where John Eastwood had built a log cabin in earlier years, while carrying on his surveys in the area.

A logging camp was set up on the south side of the lake. Huge logs were soon sliding down the long skidways, with such terrific speed that they would leave streamers of smoke behind from friction. As they hit the water there would be a splash like a small Niagara Falls in reverse.

Work got under way on Dam 3, the smallest of the three Huntington Lake Dams, and by the time winter prevented further progress, a parapet wall seven feet high had been completed along the top of the structure. A rock quarry was opened a short distance east of Dam 2, and construction of a large crushing plant started nearby. A smaller plant was built near the main entrance to Huntington Lake Lodge. Work trains soon were shuttling back and forth from the top of the main incline, up which all material and equipment coming into Big Creek by rail was handled. The shrieking of locomotive whistles and the clanging of bells made the area sound like a main line railroad yard. Much of the work was carried on around the clock. Progress was halted when the operator of the large incline hoist went to sleep while the car was on its way up from Big Creek —it took half an hour for the ascent—and was awakened when the car came crashing through the hoist house and over the top of the hoist. He barely had time to shut off the power; otherwise, he would have been pinned beneath the car. He did not wait for his time check.

Thanksgiving came along and an excellent dinner was served in each camp. On the tables in Camp 1-E, serving the Dam 3 job, the waiters—"flunkies," in construction parlance—had arranged attractive and appropriate decorations. Don Morgan and Ned Woodbury, both from the Los Angeles Office, were much intrigued with the display of "mountain holly," peculiar to the Huntington Lake area —so they were told by the flunkies. Don was tipped off and saw a chance for some "foul" play—being very good at such—at the expense of Woodbury. The latter was quite anxious to get some of the "holly" to take back to Los Angeles, and with encouragement from

Morgan, it was arranged for the head flunkie to escort Woodbury down the rugged and brushy Big Creek Canyon so he could select and pick his own. Naturally, such a rare bush grew in places difficult of access. When the head flunkie decided Woodbury had had enough scrambling through the brush, getting scratched and his clothes torn, he stopped at an unusually attractive manzanita bush. He broke off several small branches, stripped some leaves, then took some cranberries from his pocket and gently stuck them on the ends of the branches—at the same time saying, "Mr. Woodbury, there is your 'mountain holly'." In the meantime, Don Morgan had disappeared.

We were able to continue work, with minor interruptions from storms, until Christmas Day, when we had to dig out of four feet of snow. The major activity for the remainder of the winter was centered at Big Creek, where a small crew was stationed to unload cement and place it in storage in preparation for the following spring, when work would be resumed at Huntington Lake. This routine was upset about 4:00 p.m. on February 19, 1917. A few of us in the office heard a heavy thump, followed shortly by an excited call from R. B. Lawton, in charge of operation. A break had occurred in one of the penstocks (pipe lines) half way up the mountain. They could not close, from the plant, the 42-inch gate at the top of the penstock—and could I send some men up there at once to close it. That was a tough order—the break could not have occurred at a worse time, as the snow even at Big Creek was deep enough to require travel by sled, and it was still snowing hard. Three of us left at once with three horses, hitched tandem to a long, narrow sled called a "snow boat." We were unable to proceed beyond Huntington Lake Lodge, as no trail had been broken and the snow was too deep for the horses. We loaded the heavy duty jacks and other tools on to a large toboggan. Wearing snowshoes, we started for the gate house, about a mile distant, pulling the load. After much floundering, and fighting a blizzard all the way, with only a kerosene lantern for light, we reached the gate house about 2:00 a.m., eventually getting the gate jacked shut. It is disconcerting to note the only item appearing in the power house's log book is "Gate was jacked down"— nothing to indicate the unusual difficulties experienced by those closing it.

Whenever a power house generator is idle because of breakdown, all hands concentrate their efforts on restoring it to service. One was idle now. A special heavy laminated steel bulkhead was quickly designed and made in Los Angeles to blank off the broken branch of the penstock pipe. Upon arrival, it was man-handled by sled to the site of the break, well up the mountain, and bolted in place. It was then possible for water to flow through the other branch and operate the affected unit at reduced output with one water wheel. By working day and night, repairs were completed and normal service restored on March 1.

Starr thought I needed a change, and suggested I take advantage of the opportunity of a slack period, for a month or so. He knew I was planning to be married. His suggestion made the step definite, and I left at once for the Middle West. One of the many jobs completed the previous fall at Huntington Lake, preparatory to raising the dams, was the building of five cottages. I had hinted at the time I would appreciate having one.

In spite of precautions on my part, the local espionage system worked to perfection as to the arrival of the newlyweds at Big Creek a month later. No better advertising was ever accomplished. When the S. J. & E. train was within half a mile of the Big Creek depot, "Spike" Meehan at the throttle, all Hell broke loose—the fireman had a full head of steam ready for the occasion. The locomotive whistle was the signal for the other engines in the area to join in, as well as the machine shop. They kept it up until we alighted at the station, when bedlam broke out there. The entire school had been dismissed so all could be on hand to add to the noise. All available employees were present to do their part. Wash tubs, wash basins, tin cans—anything and everything that could be used to advantage for noise-making—had been commandeered. We were escorted to a much-decorated conveyance—one of the huge Shaver lumber wagons. Six shiny black mules, their harness wrapped with white cloth, were hitched to the outfit, and perched on the high driver's seat, black-faced, and in livery attire, was General Foreman Bill Whitmire. He even had on white gloves. A canopied seat for the bridal couple was arranged far below the driver, in the center of the long wagon bed. Hanging all around the wagon were dozens of tin cans, more dragged on the ground behind, and dozens of old shoes completed the decorations. The parade started—we were driven around Big Creek to the accompaniment of the noisy throng that followed, finally being allowed to alight at one of A. O. Smith's hotel tents, which was to be our home for about a month. About ten p.m., as soon as the lights were out, rocks began to rattle over the corrugated iron roof. The stove began to smoke, as a cover had been placed over the chimney. Visitors had arrived—we had to have fresh air, so they were invited to come in. One carried a Victrola, another a coffee percolator, others brought food, and although the tent was crowded, the party made themselves at home until morning. Taken altogether, it was a reception we have never forgotten.

The latter part of April brought signs of life again in the Huntington Lake area, and by the middle of May a beehive in blossom time could not have been busier.

On April 30, Mrs. Redinger and I entered our new cottage, but to do so, much shovel work was necessary as the snow extended above the top of the front door.

Special quarters had been built the previous fall in one corner of the lodge grounds for the department of Auditor C. P. Staal, whose representative on the job was C. R. Duncan. Not only did men have to be paid, but the amount of accounting for such a job naturally was large. It was more practical to handle all such work locally rather than in Los Angeles. Starr's office was also in the accounting department building.

Crews got busy, concentrating on Dam No. 3, where their work had been abandoned the previous fall. New excavation had to be made along the downstream toe of each dam for the new concrete section. Pneumatic drills started pounding away on the back of the dam, drilling holes for the steel rails to be used as reinforcements to bond the new concrete to the old. Carpenters were as thick as flies, building forms and long chutes to carry the concrete. One might think of the new concrete slab as a huge blanket covering the entire lower side and top of each structure. Bill Whitmire called the attention of Tom O'Connor, one of the carpenter foremen, to the lost motion in keeping ahead with the concrete forms. O'Connor had an alibi when he pointed to one of his men carrying a two-by-four, emphasizing that the carpenter was not waiting for the helper. Just then the carpenter set the two-by-four down to gaze around. Whitmire inquired as to the need for such relaxation, whereupon O'Connor quickly countered with, "He's thinkin' now and plannin' his next move."

An unusually large gyratory rock crusher was being installed in the main aggregate plant between Dam 2 and the quarry. After climbing through a regular forest of trestle timbers one morning, I introduced myself to the man handling the installation. He said his name was "Smith"—a most uncommon one, I remarked. This was the way I first met T. A. Smith, who became one of our best foremen, with many years of service at the time of his early death. He was best known as "T. A." and was also called "Hard-Boiled" Smith, but all a man had to do to get along with him was put out a day's work—and "T. A." knew what constituted such.

As the Dam 3 job progressed, men moved to Dam No. 2 to make it ready for its share of the program. From Dam No. 2 the move would be to Dam No. 1, the last of the large dams to be raised in height. The excavation at the toe of Dam No. 1 was considerable, since much loose material had accumulated since completion of the original structure. The derricks were repaired as necessary and used for the excavation required for the raising program. In the removal of all of the material at the toe of Dam No. 1, a concrete mixer was uncovered, as well as a number of kegs of rusted nails.

The intake tower at Dam No. 1 had to be increased in height also. This structure stands in the lake high above the portal of the tunnel through which water flows to the plants below. Its purpose is to house the controls for operating the nine-foot tunnel gate. In addition to raising the tower, the machinery to operate the gate had to be installed and enclosed. Since the construction of the dams in 1913, the tower had functioned with a windlass arrangement, unhoused, and operated by man power.

One of the many important details of any construction job involves material—its availability when and where wanted, whether it be one hundred thousand board feet of lumber, a keg of nails or whatever. It was the duty of Harold Fox (in later years builder of the Pacific Gas and Electric Company's Balch plant) to see that no phase of the job suffered for lack of anything. He probably covered more territory daily, expediting the needs of the various jobs, than any other individual. What he did not have in his head about things available, he carried as notes in a little canvas bag suspended from his shoulder.

The arrival of summer brought guests to the lodge, which was in the center of all construction. Blasting in the quarry, a short half-mile away, occurred at all hours, especially at night. Guests who did not enjoy being severely shaken while in bed would check out, while others would complain to Manager Babb, who would ask Starr if something could not be done about it. An irate guest might even suggest firing the foreman. Starr was crowding everybody, especially the quarry crews, and I usually knew when to expect the heavy blasts. They were most likely to occur shortly after a special complaint had been made, just to give that "blankety-blank guest something to really squawk about."

The crushing and screening plant, built to serve the Dam No. 3 job, was only about two hundred feet across the track from five new cottages, one of which I occupied. Starr had the one between mine and the office building. He always slept with at least one ear open and the crushing plant could not stop during the night but what he would be out to learn the reason. Actually, I saw him climb to the top of the plant in his pajamas, at times. As I lived next door, I would either hear him when he got out, or he would see that I was awake. A large stump was blasted about 2:00 o'clock one morning. The jolt was heavy, the center of the disturbance being nearby. My 'phone rang, as I was sure it would. Starr wanted to know "what in hell" that was, since it was not near the quarry. After being told, he remarked that the quarry was bad enough, but if we were moving other blasting into the lodge grounds, he would be accused of closing down the place.

An incident most unusual in those days occurred early one morning during the summer, of interest when compared to present day customs. The mother of one of the timekeepers created a furor when she walked through the camp wearing trousers. Unfortunately for me, I happened to be near the office. Starr called me in excitedly, and wanted to know if I had seen what he saw. Of course, I had—the outfit was really good-looking, too. He wanted to know who the woman was. I found out—and it then became my job to see that the mother and son were duly impressed with the "seriousness" of such an appearance, followed by instruction that it must not occur again. How times have changed! I don't think it is any exaggeration to say that today in the mountains, at the resorts especially, it is rather unusual to see a woman in a dress.

Last to be constructed was the much smaller structure called Dam 3A, which spans the saddle between Dams 2 and 3. The end of October saw the completion of all that had been done to make Huntington Lake ready to hold nearly twice as much water the following year as previously.

X

The Merger Takes Place

THE CONSOLIDATION of the Pacific Light & Power Corporation and Southern California Edison Company was completed in June, 1917, when the rights of the former were transferred by Government permit to the latter. Although this change took place in the midst of the raising of the Huntington Lake dams, those of us engaged on that work were practically unaware of any such move. The Pacific Light & Power Corporation did not really lose its identity in this area until the Huntington Lake job was finished.

Along with this consolidation, the Mt. Whitney Power & Electric Company was also taken over. John Hays Hammond was responsible for financing the parent company. While visiting his nephew, Col. William H. Hammond, in Honolulu just before World War II, I learned of his uncle's autobiography, in which the story is told about the raising of the money.

In 1898, John Hays Hammond was in London and received a visit from his brother Bill, to interest him in organizing the Mt. Whitney Power Company, since San Francisco bankers displayed no desire to invest. Mr. Hammond writes about A. G. Wishon and Ben M. Maddox being associated with his brother in the project of pumping water by electricity for that part of the San Joaquin Valley. There was much concern on the part of Mr. Hammond as to the feasibility of sending electricity so far—a distance of thirty-five miles —and he commented that it had never been done before for irrigation. Since he was a man of unusually keen vision, the capital for launching the project was quickly supplied by him and a London banker friend, whose interest Mr. Hammond bought shortly after his return to the United States, leaving him as the sole backer.

To produce kilowatts, water is necessary. To get it, these men of real vision set out to enlarge four small lakes, fifty-five to sixty miles distant from Visalia and at elevations up to 11,000 feet. Just to explore the possibilities in such remote regions would be no small undertaking even today. Four small dams were built, utilizing local material and cement packed in on mules, and involving difficulties which would have discouraged less determined individuals. Silver, Eagle, Monarch and Franklin Lakes, high above Mineral King, functioning today as the result of super-human efforts, attest to the pioneering spirit of these men who deserve unusual credit as the forerunners of electric power in Visalia and vicinity.

The parent company, reincorporated in 1909 as the Mt. Whitney Power and Electric Company, started in business with a connected load of approximately seven hundred horsepower.

It is my good fortune to have known Mr. Wishon and Mr. Maddox in later years, while the former was president of the San Joaquin Light & Power Corporation, Fresno, and Mr. Maddox headed the Mt. Whitney Power and Electric Company in Visalia. I shall never forget their unusual experiences as pioneers in the field of electric power. Mr. Wishon, when in a reminiscent mood, enjoyed describing his efforts as a salesman to promote the use of a single light bulb at fifty cents to one dollar a month in the Visalia, Tulare, Lindsay, Exeter and Porterville areas.

By 1912, the Mt. Whitney Power and Electric Company had four plants in operation—Kaweah Nos. 1, 2, 3, and Tule, the rights of the latter having been purchased from the Globe Light and Power Company in 1904 and placed in service five years later. Kaweah No. 3 and Tule plants are in operation today as originally constructed. Old Kaweah No. 1 has been replaced with a single unit in a new building. Kaweah No. 2 has been modernized with a new unit in place of the old one. The original buckets on the water wheels of the two Tule plant units have been in use continuously to date, and only now are about ready for replacement. One of the original units of the old Kaweah No. 1 plant now stands as a monument on the site where it turned out kilowatts for so many years. A bronze plaque attests to that fact in these words:

ON THIS SITE STOOD

POWER PLANT OF MT. WHITNEY POWER CO.

THIS GENERATOR, ONE OF THREE, WAS

THE FIRST TO DELIVER ELECTRIC POWER

TO TULARE COUNTY. IT WAS IN CONTINUOUS

SERVICE JUNE, 1899, TO MAY, 1929.

SOUTHERN CALIFORNIA EDISON COMPANY

Incidentally, I know of no book more inspiring and fascinating than the autobiography of John Hays Hammond, a California mining engineer who became an international figure.

Dam 2 at Huntington Lake from top of crusher.

Right: Big Creek 150,000 volt transmission lines in 1917.

Below: Big Creek transmission lines at Saugus in 1930. Capacity of lines was raised to 220,000 volts in 1923.

XI

Building a Transmission Line

DAM 3A WAS ABOUT COMPLETED when Starr asked me to move to the San Joaquin Valley and complete the East Big Creek transmission line. The two lines, each 150,000 volts, were to have been completed between Big Creek and Los Angeles in 1913. Partly for financial reasons, the east line was left with a one-hundred-four mile gap between Bakersfield and Kings River. The necessary tower steel, aluminum conductors, insulators etc. had been purchased and delivered to the nearest railroad stations through the Valley in 1913.

Although I had no such experience, I set out to get four camps established—one to excavate for tower footings, one to set them, the third to erect the towers, the fourth to hang insulators, string the conductors and ground wire. The last one also functioned as head-quarters for the job. The first headquarters camp was established near Richgrove.

The headaches were many—truck drivers, delivering material along the line, would leave gates open; horses, cattle, pigs and what not would get out; sometimes a horse, colt, cow or calf would get cut by barbed wire. Before I knew a gate had been left open, an irate rancher would be on my neck. A field, or some kind of crop, would suffer from our trucks. Sometimes damage would be imaginary, but all complaints were not only listened to, but followed up. One frequent source of trouble was right-of-way problems. All property owners were notified of our intentions, and their permission asked before we entered. Many were surprised to learn, because of change of ownership, that the right-of-way for two lines had been obtained originally. Trips were made with a number of them to the court house in each county where our lines were involved to show them the record. Mr. Sheridan, of Orange Cove, appeared one day to show me something which made him most angry. In a far corner of a very nice young olive orchard, he pointed to a sick-looking tree. Then, calling my attention to truck tracks, he reached over and lifted the tree out of the ground. The driver, in delivering steel for a tower nearby, had backed his truck over the tree, breaking it off. Instead of reporting it, he stood the tree up and heaped enough dirt around to keep it upright. By the time the tree attracted the owner's attention, the truck driver had left the job.

Ben Maddox was called on many times. Whenever I met up with a "rabid" rancher—one whom I could not reconcile—I would make a trip to Visalia. Mr. Maddox not only knew every individual in the entire area, but was highly respected by all. There was never a case involving a third party in which he was not able to help make an amicable settlement. Not infrequently, he would accompany me to the home of someone who felt he had a serious complaint. Eventually, Mr. Maddox, whenever I appeared at his office, would throw his head back and exclaim, with his hearty laugh, "Well, Dave, who is chasing you out of the country now?"

In those days, the conductors were pulled to tension with a four-up team of mules. While the crew was working near Visalia they experienced some trouble with small boys, who were vitally interested in such operations. One particular group was warned several times to keep its distance. Before the crew was aware of it, one youngster had taken hold of the conductor being raised and was too far above the ground to let loose, as he could have been seriously injured by the fall. By the time the team could be stopped, the boy was twenty-five feet in the air. Men began yelling at him to drop, which he finally had to do, being saved from injury by being caught.

When the kid was turned loose, he hit the ground running—he had had enough.

During the summer the tower steel would get so hot it could not be handled without gloves. It was not unusual for pieces to be found missing. Piles of it had been stored in railroad yards along the way for several years and some was hidden by heavy growths of weeds. Now and then a station agent, new at the location, would know nothing of its presence. The heavy tower legs topped the list of shortages. Such pieces made excellent material for fence repairs. A trip around the local ranches always resulted in our finding missing members, small pieces were found around chicken yards. Identification was not difficult as the original stenciling was legible, and property owners never voiced any objection about removal. Having noticed the material for several years covered with weeds, they took for granted that it could not be of much importance. Because of World War I, aluminum was valuable; consequently, the reels of cable were never left unguarded along the line while waiting to be strung.

In taking over this job, it was necessary that I learn to drive a car. Being furnished a Ford pick-up with Walter Bauermeister as instructor, I took the thing out along a little-used dirt road. Ever since, I can fully appreciate the feelings of anyone learning to drive, and especially how narrow a really wide highway can appear to be. Later, Jack Wheeler sent me a car which, even today, I recall as a most wonderful automobile. The Stevens-Duryea roadster, Edison No. 3, more familiarly called the "3 Spot," was a real car even though it was nine years old at the time it was passed along to me. Cranked by hand, it was the only car I have ever driven that would start when warm merely by my turning on the ignition, provided it hadn't stood for more than fifteen or twenty minutes.

Mrs. Redinger was the only woman in the four camps. We had a twelve by fourteen tent. It is amazing what she accomplished in making our "rag house" comfortable—even when the time came for a Christmas tree. We moved every month or six weeks, camping in pastures, cut-over wheat or barley fields, some of which were newly plowed; one site was a stream bed. It was nothing unusual for interested cows or hogs to become tangled in the tent ropes, and their curiosity seemed to reach its peak at night. In general, our whole outfit was more or less frowned upon by the populace as we moved through the country. We seemed to be shunned as though we were gypsies. Mrs. Redinger, in her day-time loneliness, struck up a conversation one afternoon with a young woman who was working in an adjoining field, driving a team hitched to a harrow. Always fond of horses, she indicated that fact, and her anxiety to do her part in the war-time effort. The stranger was interested, and I took Mrs. Redinger to the distant ranch house at six o'clock the following morning. Imagine her dismay, after anticipating a grand time driving the team, when she was informed by the ranch woman that the washing was ready, water was hot, etc. Rising to the occasion, and not to be outdone, she pitched into a stack of dirty clothes such as she had never seen outside a laundry. I returned between five and six o'clock that evening and found her just finishing. The premises reminded me of a circus—everything in the yard on all sides of the house, including the fences, was covered with drying clothes. The ranch woman was much chagrined the following day to learn from Mrs. Redinger that she had no intention of charging for the work, would accept nothing—and would have enjoyed the harrowing much more.

We experienced the usual difficulty in obtaining and keeping cookhouse help. This was particularly true of cooks. They were, perhaps, more temperamental than is usual because of the nature of the work, since the camps moved frequently. One winter morning before daylight, the camp foreman walked over to our tent to report that the chef had gone and there was no one to get breakfast. Mrs. Redinger heard the conversation and came to the rescue, saying that if she could have some help she would get up and do the cooking until another chef could be found. The men went to work at their usual hour, and the meals were reported to be most satisfactory. In fact, there was much reluctance on the part of the large crew to make a change. However, a chef was secured late the following day, and another of the episodes common to the cookhouses was at an end.

In the beginning, I tried to discourage Mrs. Redinger from joining me under the conditions as I knew they would be. In spite of this, she looked forward with deep anticipation to living in a tent. She has always held the viewpoint that a wife's place is with her husband and her duty is to make him as comfortable as possible regardless of where he has to be located. Not only was the isolation difficult for her—I was gone all day almost every day, week after week, month in and month out—but the summer heat in the valley was almost unbearable at times, in spite of our having a large canvas fly over the tent. In most of our camp locations there was not a shade tree within miles. On more than one occasion, when I returned in the afternoon I would find her wrapped in a wet sheet, and one suspended at either end of the tent. I am sure I will be pardoned when I say she deserves a world of credit for the part she has played, not only under conditions as she found them on the transmission line, but all through the construction camp life in which she has lived during our married years.

By September we had reached Kings River, and were about ready to break camp. E. R. Davis, retired senior vice president of the Southern California Edison Company, in company with Don Morgan and Bob Lawton, arrived early one morning to inform me that Arthur Blight needed help to complete some surveys in the Big Creek country before bad weather set in.

XII

Jackass Meadows and Vermilion Valley

THE MOUNTAINS HAVE MANY so-called "Jackass Meadows," and the Sierra is no exception. H. B. Howard had a survey party working in Upper Jackass Meadow, on the South Fork of the San Joaquin River a few miles below Blaney Meadows. At the time we were there, in 1918, the duck pond at the upper end of the meadow was known as "Florence Lake," having been so named about 1900 by a camper, Starr, for his daughter. The surveys we were making played their part in the later development of Florence Lake reservoir, dam and tunnel.

We had the whole back country pretty much to ourselves in those days. The road did not extend beyond the lower end of Huntington Lake, and packing concessions were few. Occasionally, we would see a cattle man or forest ranger, but seldom a tourist. A camp could be left indefinitely without being molested by humans. What a contrast with conditions as they are today! Cabins which have been built and stocked for use of hydrographers during winter months are not safe even though padlocked. "Private Property" signs mean nothing to some who now come to the mountains. Formerly, if a prospector, cattle man, or such had any occasion to help himself to a food cache, or use a cabin, he was welcome—a note would always be left, or word passed along in some manner to the owner. Such was the law of the mountains. Today, locks are broken, windows smashed, chains cut, and property taken or destroyed, without any regard for anything or anybody. As the result of automobiles and extended roads, a new breed of people has found its way into the mountains.

The latter part of September we moved to the central part of Vermilion Valley for reconnaissance, establishing our camp on Mono Creek. The valley is reported to have been given its name by Theodore S. Solomons in 1894. We came across the name of this party frequently, as having visited these parts during the later years of the past century and the first of the present one. The color of the cliffs at the upper end of the valley, no doubt, is the reason for the name of both.

We were investigating the feasibility of water storage, which, of course, would include a suitable site for a dam. These surveys were, in part at least, the forerunners of the Mono-Bear development which came along ten years later.

In those days, fishing in some of the mountain streams, and particularly Mono Creek, was what the "Ike Waltons" really dream about. Although a limit of fifty trout had been established in 1905, it was seldom reached, as we caught no more than would be eaten. There were few fishing licenses in evidence in those days, although the first, according to the Division of Fish and Game, were issued at one dollar in 1913, the fee being increased to two dollars in 1927. For the type of people frequenting the mountains in the years about which I am writing, there was not much need for licenses or limits —certainly not the latter.

September changed to October, then November—and not only were the days growing shorter, but the nights colder. For a while after our move we could enjoy a bath in Mono Creek, or thought we did by kidding ourselves. Even in mid-summer, the temperature of such mountain streams seldom rises much above sixty degrees, and when ice started forming at night we thought it was time to think about the hot springs as a more appropriate place for a bath.

Located on the South Fork of the San Joaquin River about three miles below Vermilion Valley, Mono Hot Springs was a favorite stop-over to break a hot and dusty trail trip. Long before present-day facilities, the U. S. Forest Service had installed a large concrete tub at the principal spring, sheltered by a roughly constructed shake cabin. A sign cautioned all users not to remain in the bath more than twenty minutes—to stay longer would result in a devitalizing effect, and impair one's health. Through the years, the old tub was enjoyed by many passersby. As usual, one found many names, initials, and such wisecracks as are found in public places. I recall seeing one somewhat unusual. Two Big Creek couples, one chaperoning the other, had enjoyed restful baths. Each had registered his or her name in a group on the wall, with the comment, "What a wonderful bath." Some jokester, taking advantage of the opportunity, had pencilled beneath, "Ye Gods, what a tub full."

Mono Hot Springs grew in popularity with the Japanese for three or four years prior to World War II—in fact, they really took over the place. Whole families moved in and remained for the season; consequently, it was not so popular with other campers during that period. This should be said, however: the white caretakers reported on different occasions that the Japanese always left the bath houses immaculate, which is more than could be said for other users.

The morning of November 11 arrived—the year, of course, was 1918. Being the first to arise after the cook, and having observed the weather, I noticed that the sky was overcast and snow was starting to fall. Our pack train had just arrived from Huntington Lake the night before—with Dave Qualls in charge. Such an arrival was indeed timely. Word was passed around that everybody had better "shake a leg" and get going, as the weather was acting as if it meant business. Breakfast was quickly eaten, beds rolled, tents taken down, and everything made ready for the packers. By 8:30 o'clock, the whole outfit started for Huntington Lake. It should be mentioned again that there were no roads above the lower end of the lake. The snowflakes grew in size and frequency, and the ground was shortly covered with a white blanket. The trail became increasingly difficult for the pack animals. The mules appeared to sense the necessity of getting over Kaiser Pass as quickly as possible and did not lose very much time in their observations as they moved along. Pack mules have always entertained me. There was an unusually wise one on this trip. He was carrying an extra wide load of bed rolls, with the camp cook stove on top. Frequently, I would notice him size up the clearance between trees, and if he decided it was too narrow, he would back up and go around. That particular mule, during his many trips that fall, never had an accident in losing or damaging a pack. We did not want to stop for lunch, but ate our hurriedly prepared sandwiches on the fly. We thought we did not even dare take the time to stop at the hot springs for a much-needed bath. Travel over the trail was growing more difficult for the pack animals, all of which had been loaded more heavily than usual in order to allow each man one animal to ride. Three o'clock in the afternoon found us on Kaiser Pass, elevation 9305 feet. The snow was up to the animals' bellies, and we had to raise our feet in the stirrups to clear. We reached the upper end of Huntington Lake about six o'clock. Ever since five it had been dark. We had been hearing whistles blowing at Big Creek, and an occasional heavy report of a powder blast. We were so cold we did not pay much attention to the noise, but did wonder finally what the ruckus was all about. It suddenly dawned on us that maybe the war was over. No one ever traveled a trail that seemed so long as from the upper end of Huntington Lake around the lower end, past the Lodge and on to Camp 1A, near Dam 1—a distance of about eight trail miles.

As soon as we arrived in camp I tried to call Big Creek. No one would answer a telephone for quite a while. In the meantime, the noise appeared to be on the increase. After much ringing, someone at the other end yelled, "Hell's Bells, we haven't time to talk—the war's over."

The next two months I spent with a crew, increasing clearances of conductors in the spans of the Big Creek transmission lines that cross some of the highways in the vicinity of Visalia.

Then, after a trip to Independence, California, to search through the old files of the U. S. Government Land Office for information relative to original surveys of land occupied by the Edison Company, I went to the Kern River No. 3 Project as assistant to Resident Engineer Capt. F. J. Mills. The Edison Company had decided to speed up completion of that development, involving miles of tunnels, installation of power house, penstocks etc. The power house was well started, when, in February, 1920, after a very busy year, I returned to Big Creek as assistant to Resident Engineer Arthur Blight.

XIII

Shaver Tunnel

THERE HAS BEEN considerable activity for many years in the lumber industry throughout the area extending from Toll-house to Dinkey Creek. The first saw mill above Tollhouse was built by Moses Mack and John W. Humphries in 1867 near Pine Ridge. Another one was set up in 1881 at Ockenden, a few miles below Shaver Lake.

The lake got its name from C. B. Shaver, a Michigan lumber man who came to California and was a co-founder of the Fresno Flume & Irrigation Company, incorporated October 31, 1891, to make and deal in lumber. To have large storage space for logs and to float them to the saw mill, a sizable body of water was required. The site selected for the mill and pond was formerly known as Stevenson Basin and Meadows. To create the pond, a rock-fill dam, forty feet high and about three hundred feet long, was built across Stevenson Creek at the mill-site, thus forming the original Shaver Lake, elevation 5275 feet with a capacity of around five thousand acre feet. Mrs. Shaver, whom I knew very well, told me the dam was built in 1893. When she first arrived to join her husband on July 4 of that year, riding behind a team of oxen, she found him busy with a crew of men on its construction.

Lumber was delivered to the San Joaquin Valley in a unique manner, since it was floated through a flume from the mill to Clovis, sixty flume miles distant. Abandoned in 1917, the flume has almost disappeared, except for one long trestle which can be seen today clinging to the cliff high on Mt. Stevenson, also called "Flume Point." The water in which the lumber floated was released for irrigation after reaching Clovis. During the heyday of the San Joaquin & Eastern Railroad, trainmen frequently would create merriment at the expense of some timid passenger, by telling him or her, "You haven't seen anything yet—wait until we get up there," pointing to the old flume trestle two or three thousand feet above.

By court decree, the firm's name was changed on September 8, 1908, to Fresno Flume & Lumber Company. On July 30, 1919, they conveyed to the Southern California Edison Company by deed, certain lands for the present reservoir site. Adjoining properties were conveyed as of August 1, 1919, to the Shaver Lake Lumber Company, which had been incorporated for that purpose. Including the reservoir site, a total of some 32,000 acres was involved, a large portion of which had been logged during the previous twenty-five years.

When the year 1920 came along, it found the Edison Company operating the saw mill, and a heavy construction program getting under way, with every indication of its continuing for some years. Involved were quite a number of power houses, dams, tunnels, roads etc. Lumber was needed for such a vast program. Scattered trees were being put through the mill and they not only provided lumber, but also cleared the area destined to become the enlarged Shaver Lake reservoir.

At Big Creek, cottages, shops, mess hall, warehouses, and quarters for a large clerical force had to be built. Provided for the latter was a three-story building adjacent to the new headquarters office. Facilities had to be made available for supplying medical attention, and a hospital was constructed—Dr. H. M. McNeil taking charge on February 1, 1920. This was the first of three base hospitals, the other two coming along a year or so later. The lumber had to be hauled from the Shaver mill by heavy wagons to the San Joaquin & Eastern

Railroad at Shaver Crossing. The main highway was not oiled, and winter storms made it almost impassable. An eight-up team at times would literally drag the huge wagons through mud hub-deep. On one occasion a wagon, upon arrival at the railroad, carried only four 4 by 4's, all that remained of the original load, which had to be lightened along the way.

My house, like all other new structures, was built of green lumber, which did not dry very fast in such wet weather. A large heating stove was kept going day and night, not only for warmth but to dry the house inside. In spite of the heat and the care, we found our clothes would mildew. As the boards dried, they would crack here and there, accompanied by a loud noise comparable to the shooting of a heavy rifle. There were no complaints—others had the same experience. Everybody was happy about his job, and "raring to go."

Our house was built on a sandy slope, mostly barren except for a manzanita bush here and there. Mrs. Redinger wanted to set out some fruit trees immediately. I told her it was foolish, as we would not be here long enough to enjoy any of the fruit—that no construction job lasts more than two, three or four years at the most. She went ahead and got her fruit trees—twenty-five to thirty of them. That was in 1920 and we have been enjoying the apples for more than twenty years; besides, we have given hundreds of boxes to local families, the cookhouses, and friends outside.

Several camps were built to serve the tunnel to be driven from Shaver Lake towards Power House 2, beneath Musick Mountain, named for Henry or Charles Musick, both of whom were connected with the saw mill at Shaver. The tunnel would carry water to Power House No. 2 and, subsequently, to Power House No. 2-A. Large air compressors were skidded over snow and through mud to the Camp 19 site—the adit about mid-way along the tunnel.

At Camp 29, the north portal, we had our first experience with portable frame bunkhouses. They were shipped in sections ready for assembly, and under the circumstances served very well. A large number were also set up for family use at Big Creek headquarters.

The word had been given to get the tunnel started, and when such instructions are turned loose in construction, the "dirt must fly" right now—and what's more, it usually does. The Shaver Tunnel, 14,300 feet long, eight by eleven feet in cross section, actually got under way with respect to driving, on February 5, 1920, and was completed May 6, 1921. An average crew of ninety men for each of the four headings worked continuously throughout the job. At that time we considered the progress to be excellent. In one heading, an advance of 522 feet was made in a thirty-day period. Equipment included air-operated "Shuveloaders," or mucking machines, "Leyner" drills, pneumatic drill sharpeners, storage battery locomotives, and huge blowers for supplying fresh air. The experience with this equipment served as a valuable guide for driving other large tunnels during the next ten years.

Because the out-flow from the original lake did not justify higher head units in Power House No. 2, with an increasingly longer penstock, water from the lake was to be carried into Tunnel No. 2 through a temporary diversion tunnel and pipe line at the north portal. This water would be used in Power House No. 2 under a head of 1,860 feet, together with that coming through Tunnel No. 2 from Big Creek No. 1, until Power House No. 2-A would be built, some years hence.

Arthur Blight and I were paid our first visit by President John B. Miller with Mrs. Miller, Medical Director Dr. E. A. Bryant and Mrs. Bryant, late in the summer of 1920. We met the party, piloted by George C. Ward, at Shaver Crossing. For small groups, the San Joaquin & Eastern had a White truck chassis equipped with a special body and car wheels, adapted for travel over the rails. Instead of the regular train, our guests chose to make the trip in the White bus (also known locally as "White Elephant"). The visitors were shown, among other things, the Commissary, or store, at Camp 19. Mr. Ward reflected embarrassment when Mrs. Miller, looking over the stores, inquired about there being no Bordens milk on the shelves at the time. This went over my head, but I learned afterwards that Mrs. Miller was a Borden. It was not long until that brand put in its appearance.

In August of that same year, we received word from our Los Angeles Office to check up on the whereabouts of one of the Edison Company attorneys, who was making an investigation of a quarter-section of land within the Shaver Lake area, all of which, covered with dense brush and thickets of small trees, made searching difficult. Eventually I found him wandering and stumbling around, his shirt open, bareheaded, perspiration rolling off his face—and how glad he was to see me, even though a stranger! Such was my introduction to George E. Trowbridge, a present-day member of the Edison Company legal staff.

Coincident with completion of the tunnel, a large wooden flume, about one-half mile in length, was ready to carry Shaver Lake water from the old rock-fill dam to the tunnel intake until construction of the present dam. To utilize the additional water thus to be made available, a third unit was installed at Power House No. 2 during 1920, increasing its capacity from 45,000 to 66,000 H.P.

None of the Big Creek tunnels are lined with concrete except where it is required to support bad ground. Several places required such treatment, but less than one thousand feet of the Shaver Tunnel are lined.

After the Shaver property was purchased by the Southern California Edison Company for reservoir purposes, the Company dismantled, moved from the lake area and reassembled in what is known as "Rockhaven," adjoining the lake, the house which had been occupied by the Shaver family during the preceding summers.

XIV

Power House No. 8 Is Built

IN A PRECEDING CHAPTER, reference was made to the tunnel which was started in 1914 on a slow schedule towards Power House 3, yet to be built. Prior to June 1, 1920, the proposed plant was intended to operate under a head of about 1,400 feet. Progress on the 14 foot by 17 foot tunnel was slow, as is obvious from the fact that 2,050 feet were driven between July, 1914, and February, 1920. Late in 1919, the job was speeded up, and extension of the road was started below Power House 2 to serve the adits to be located along the tunnel.

On May 1, 1920, with a total of 8,400 feet of the extension completed, the road building was suddenly halted. Because of the urgent need for more power, drastic steps had to be taken. It was decided to abandon plans, temporarily, for Plant No. 3 and concentrate on one having a head of seven hundred feet, half that intended for the former. Such a plant, provided it was built quickly, would relieve the critical load situation until Power House No. 3 could be completed.

World War I is credited with playing a large part in the rapidly increasing load demand. Another important factor favoring the sudden change of plans was the perfection of the vertical reaction turbine to greater efficiency.

A site for the new plant was selected at the mouth of Big Creek, on the San Joaquin River. The change in plans reduced the length of the tunnel to approximately 6,000 feet, making it unnecessary

Shaver saw mill, lumber camp and the original Shaver Lake in 1926. Long timber flume connected lake with intake of Shaver tunnel.

San Joaquin and Eastern White bus (passenger car) with Conductor Walter Low in door and George C. Ward at open window.

Powerhouse No. 8, smallest in size and capacity of Big Creek powerhouses, in 1947.

to extend the road further on tunnel grade, but requiring a new location for it, the forebay, penstock and power house. The designating number "8" was assigned to the proposed plant. It has been somewhat of a puzzle to many why a power house called No. 8 is located between Nos. 2 and 3. It is because the other numbers up to eight had already been assigned in other filings with the U. S. Government.

To expedite tunnel driving, Adit No. 1 was started on February 20, 1920, and by May 17 a 20 foot by 20 foot section, 193 feet long, had been driven. From this point the crews could turn in opposite directions and work two additional headings in the main tunnel— one towards the intake, the other towards the outlet. It was then decided to enlarge it to the adit size and use standard steam shovels, Marion 40's, operated with compressed air, for loading the muck or blasted rock. Up to May 5, 1920, there had been 2,415 feet of the original 14 foot by 17 foot size driven; the remainder was finished to the adit size.

Instead of the usual type of surge chamber at the outlet of a pressure tunnel, the one provided for Big Creek 8 is a large steel tank, 35 feet in diameter and 95 feet in height. At the bottom, outlets are provided for three penstocks, of which there are now two, one for each unit.

Camp No. 31 had been built near the mouth of the adit, and No. 32 established near the outlet. The "30" series of numbers had been assigned for use on the Big Creek 3 construction, but because of the change in plans, that plant had to share them with No. 8.

The number of camps was increasing rapidly, and with prospects for many more we decided to go into the hog business. Garbage disposal is an important item, especially for large construction camps. Instead of burning it every day, the fattening of hogs seemed a more satisfactory solution, besides offering some promise of being profitable. If we should break even, it would be worthwhile. Several hundred pigs were placed in locations readily accessible from one or more camps, a tender put in charge, and the pork project was launched. We also had a real veterinarian, "Doc" Dwight, who not only watched over the hogs but the many horses and mules scattered over the job.

The first track-laying caterpillar type of steam shovel, a revolving Marion 21, to appear on the Big Creek Project went to work on November 1, 1920. It served as prime mover in excavating the present road to the site where Camp 33, for power house workmen, was to be built. Construction of the camp was begun before completion of the road to it; in fact, it was ready for occupancy by three hundred men shortly before Christmas. The "rag houses," with floors, sprang up like mushrooms. Almost before the shovel crew had time to wash up after reaching the site, the sound of the steel triangle, so familiar in construction camps, was calling men to the first meal.

The two-mile incline to serve No. 8, longest on the San Joaquin & Eastern Railroad, was built to Camp 42, also known as Feeney, after its first foreman.

General Foreman Bill Whitmire was crowding the various phases of the work, getting excavation under way for the power house and the penstock. A short tunnel was built to by-pass Big Creek water around the power house site during the excavation and construction. Dam 5 was being built across Big Creek just below Power House No. 2, to form the Power House No. 8 forebay at the intake of its tunnel.

The large generator was shipped for assembly in the field, including "stacking the iron." Load limitation on the incline was the main reason for such field work. Not to lose any time on installation of the turbine and generator, an unusual procedure was followed for assembly of the latter. A tower of heavy timbers was built to support a large platform twenty feet above the turbine.

While the 30,000 H.P. vertical Francis-Pelton turbine was being installed, the 22,500-kilowatt General Electric generator was being assembled on the platform, both being fenced in gradually by the power house. As the building grew in height, so did the foundation beneath the generator, which did not have to be disturbed except to be lowered slightly to its permanent position after assembly.

While on a trip to New York in January and February, 1921, I visited the I. P. Morris Department of William Cramp & Sons, Philadelphia, where the hydraulic part of the unit for No. 8 was being made. A telegram from Construction Engineer Harry Dennis in Los Angeles contained the sad news that Arthur Blight had been seriously injured at Big Creek on February 14, as the result of being dragged by his horse. I was to return at once.

Besides regular pick and shovel work, the excavation for the power house was carried on by hydraulic sluicing and a revolving steam shovel, using oil for fuel. This shovel was replaced shortly by a larger Marion 40 to speed up the work. The small one was moved to a higher level to pass material down to the larger, which loaded the dump cars for final disposal. Air hammers were used extensively, as much blasting was required for breaking the hard gray granite throughout the lower foundation area. Ten and a half tons of forty per cent gelatin powder were used for the blasting. Besides the area for the foundation of one unit, an additional area was excavated for future installation, to avoid damaging the first unit at such a time. The first concrete was poured on May 12, 1921, and exactly ninety days later, on August 10, water flowed through the penstock and the unit rolled. Three days later it was generating power, establishing a record for such construction, made possible by working two shifts on the building and three on the equipment installation.

The plant had been in operation only a few days when the penstock broke at 5:39 A.M., August 20, 1921, not far above the building. The tear in the huge pipe occurred in such a way as to direct the water, rushing out under full pressure, against the east side of the generator room, where a temporary covering of corrugated iron had been placed, with an eye to future extension of the building. Such a cover served as no barrier for the water, which tore through it as though the wall were tissue paper, and into the generator room and transformer bay, carrying with it timbers, concrete and debris. The 150,000 volt leads were grounded, and about five hundred feet of penstock at the upper end collapsed. With all hands working around the clock we were able to have service restored on September 13.

Big Creek No. 8, Big Creek No. 1 and Big Creek No. 2, operated at 150,000 volts each for transmission until May, 1923, when the entire Big Creek system was changed to 220,000 volts, the first commercial use of such high voltage in the world.

About the first of September, 1921, a sizable pack party was arranged by Harry Dennis, with Fred Fowler, District Engineer of the U. S. Forest Service. To obtain stream flow data, gauging stations had to be installed, and this party was to select the locations. The two-week trip would also allow each member of the party, particularly Mr. Fowler, to visit the places under investigation for possible power development. Mr. W. A. Brackenridge, Senior Vice President of the Edison Company, started with us, but turned back after our first night at Mono Hot Springs, since he did not feel equal to the trip. We visited Blaney Meadows and Vermilion Valley, went over Silver Pass and down through Fish Creek—where the mosquitoes hadn't had a square meal for weeks. We selected several sites for gauging stations, looked over many places along the west side of the San Joaquin River, and finally reached Miller's Bridge and Mammoth Pool. Each morning we were up early, had breakfast, and were in the saddle before six o'clock. In the afternoon we would stop early enough for the fishermen in the party to provide enough trout for supper. Harry Dennis, always allergic to onions, was involved in the only incident to mar the trip for him, when some culprit placed one in his bed roll. The effect was about the same as having limburger put in the finger of one's glove.

On August 13, 1922, President John B. Miller, Mrs. Miller, their son and daughter, Morris and Carrita, accompanied by Mr. George C. Ward, arrived for their first camping trip in the Sierra. Mr. Miller inspected the various jobs under way, as the party proceeded by automobile from Hairpin over the Lower Road. Messrs. Davis, Blight and I escorted the party next day from Huntington Lake Lodge as far as Ward Lake. The road had not yet been completed beyond that point. We put the visitors on their horses in the care of H. B. Howard, one of our engineers. They left for their camp, which had been set up near the river at the lower end of Upper Jackass Meadow, the reservoir site for Florence Lake.

The most active member of the party was Mike, the wire-haired terrier. Such wide open spaces presented an entirely new world for him—so much so that he jumped out of the kayak to chase a chipmunk. He did not catch up with the pack train, and consequently there was much concern when he didn't show up in camp that night. The lost dog was well-advertised in the various camps, and diligent search was made, but without results. On the fourth day after his disappearance, the foreman of the road crew appeared in the Miller camp with the bedraggled and foot-sore pooch, barely able to wag his stubby tail. Just to have him back was ample cause for rejoicing. There was no cause for further worry during the remainder of the stay in camp, as Mike never left its site.

During his ten-day outing, Mr. Miller took full advantage of his opportunity and, steered by Howard, saw much of the country, some of which was then being prepared to furnish water for more kilowatts for the people of California.

A second failure at Big Creek No. 8 occurred at 8:40 A.M. on New Year's Day, 1924, taking two lives, when a section of the penstock broke, some distance above the power house. The rush of water down the steep hillside destroyed completely a cottage in which an employee's wife and his sister were sleeping. The upper end of the penstock collapsed again. Although the necessary repairs constituted a major job, they were made and service resumed on January 16. I happened to be returning from another trip to New York, and at Kansas City my attention was attracted to a press report of the disaster. In 1924 and 1925, steel reinforcing bands were placed around the penstock pipe—which was American made—and lap-welded, to prevent further failures.

XV
Big Creek No. 3 Development

BEFORE THE COMPLETION of Power House No. 8, plans had been revised to extend the road down the San Joaquin River Canyon to serve the Big Creek No. 3 development. The road was favored instead of three cable-operated inclines, each one of which would serve the adits proposed for the large No. 3 tunnel. The inclines would have served only during construction of the tunnel, whereas the road would always be necessary for use between plants. There was little difference in the cost of the two methods.

On August 10, 1921, construction was started to extend the road down the canyon below Power House No. 8. W. A. (Bill) Whitmire continued as general foreman on this and the entire development of Project No. 3.

Manager of Construction E. R. Davis and I decided to look at Stevenson Creek, which the road would have to cross. That creek is the natural outlet for Shaver Lake, and at times carries a considerable amount of water. We left the trail high up on the mountain and worked our way down to a saddle near the river, about two miles below the creek, where we tied our horses. We could not have picked a hotter day, and we were in excellent rattlesnake country. We crawled through and under thick brush. We slipped and slid all over rock ledges along the steep mountain side, all the way to Stevenson Creek and back to our horses, which had enjoyed the four hours' rest in the shade. We made a good guess on the location of the bridge, as the spot where we reached the creek was the one hit exactly by the road crew several months later. We had no hand level and no survey had been made—it was a case of estimating elevations.

We had several railroad steam shovels. The caterpillar type in such a size were not yet in general use. The former were equipped to operate on a standard gauge railroad track. One of these was eating its way down the canyon, using compressed air furnished by a four-inch pipe line which followed closely. Another crew started from Hairpin, the opposite end of the road, on December 1. This latter crew made more rapid progress, as there was less rock encountered than on the upper portion of the road.

As each of the three different adit locations was reached by either crew, camp would be built and preparations would proceed for tunnel driving.

Cuts in solid granite, fifty to one hundred feet high, were not uncommon. One section, about a quarter of a mile long, was blasted through hardest granite. The forty-five degree slope presented a problem, as there were no footholds from which to start work, and these had to be made by men hanging on ropes anchored to trees or rocks as much as five hundred feet above.

Between August 10, 1921, and May 30, 1922, the "Lower Road," eleven miles in length between Power House 8 and Hairpin, on the San Joaquin & Eastern Railroad, was completed by three crews working continuously. Shortly thereafter, the one and one-half mile branch to the site for Power House No. 3 was built. Preference was given the road to serve the tunnel, which had to be ready a year and half hence to coincide with completion of the power house.

During the road construction a certain route was desirable in the vicinity of Mill Creek. By purchasing an eighty-acre homestead

Right: Standard railroad steam shovel in tunnel 3.

Below: Steam shovel working at upper end of most difficult construction section of Lower Road. San Joaquin River lies below.

*Edison Company officials are
hosts for members of
California Railroad Commission
at Big Creek No. 3
on September 1, 1923.*

*Right: Cliff Dwellers' bunk
tents at Camp 35.*

which had been unoccupied for years, we could have the more favorable route. The property had stood at $250.00 for years unsold, but when it came time to buy it, the price had risen to $2,500.00. Even so, several times that figure was saved by being able to build over the more direct and easier route.

Tunnel 3, without even allowing for over-break in driving, is larger in cross-section, 21 feet by 21 feet, than any other on the Big Creek Project. At the time it was driven it was advantageous to provide for future installation of units in the power house; that is why the present capacity of three thousand feet is double what is now required.

Railroad type Marion steam shovels, operated by compressed air, with 16-foot boom and 11-foot dipper sticks, were used in the headings. Eight-ton combination battery and trolley locomotives hauled the muck from the shovels in cars of ten cubic yards capacity, which were built on the job. Under average conditions, a shovel would clean up a 15 foot round, about 450 cubic yards, of loose material, in from seven to ten hours. The best progress made in a heading in any one month was 476 feet, a record at that time for a hard rock tunnel of that size. The Ingersoll-Rand Company developed a special type of drill, known as Model X-70, for handling steel of from sixteen to twenty-four foot lengths. One of these was tried in the tunnel, with results good enough to justify its adoption.

The shortage of experienced machine men, a situation attributed to World War I, made it necessary for us to train them, in view of the large amount of tunnel work we had under way. Beginners would start as "chuck tenders," changing drill steel in the machines at a tunnel heading. Occasionally it has been necessary to explain that *this* was their duty instead of waiting on tables in mess halls.

Prior to completion of the "Lower Road," a diamond drill was skidded down the mountain side from Hairpin, to explore foundation possibilities at the site selected for Power House No. 3, and it continued drilling until early the following year. Actual excavation for the power house was started on June 5, 1922, and completed on January 10, 1923. During the excavation, made with one of the larger size railroad steam shovels, three human skeletons were uncovered at a depth of twenty feet. They were taken to be those of Indians, as an unusually good specimen of a stone axe was found nearby. Presumably they had been covered that deep with material washed in by the river through the years.

During the latter part of 1922, Mill Creek, which empties into the river at the power house site, went on a rampage. The water broke over into the site being excavated, and shortly all that could be seen of the huge steam shovel was twelve inches of the smoke stack.

A large camp for the power house construction had to be built, and was known as No. 38. One of the principal buildings was a base hospital, the second to be provided on the Big Creek Project, with Dr. G. K. Nider in charge.

It was not always easy to pick out desirable campsites, which had to be placed where the job would be served to the best advantage. Visitors seeing some of our former camp locations today are reluctant to believe we had such camps. Such is the site where Camp 35 clung to the slick rock in Stevenson Creek Canyon. The floored tents, placed on the extremely steep and rocky slope, required posts twenty to thirty feet in height on the lower side. The occupants of this camp were referred to as "cliff dwellers." Camp 34, at Adit 1, was a good runner-up for No. 35, as it hugged the cliff above the river. Camps 36 and 37, for Adit 3 and the tunnel outlet, respectively, fared much better in location.

On August 1, 1923, the last section of the tunnel was "holed through," after which the effort was concentrated towards making ready for a huge flushing of the upper half. The side walls and

Left: Bridge on Lower Road over Stevenson Creek on way to Powerhouse No. 3.

Below: Washing out tunnel 3 at adit 2, Camp 35, on August 14, 1923. John B. Miller's party is in front of mess hall.

Right: Dam 6 spills over during 1947 spring runoff. Dam and intake tower in background are below Powerhouse No. 8.

Left: Powerhouse No. 3 when completed. In 1948 another generating unit was installed, and a machine shop was added.

Below: Train load of penstock pipe for Powerhouse No. 3 is ready to leave Auberry, circa 1923.

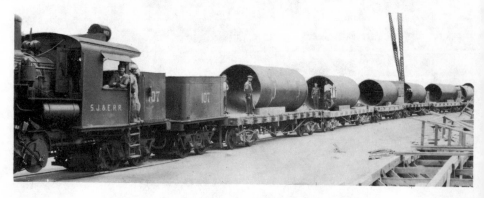

roof were given a good washing with fire hose before turning the
river through for the final washing. All such bathing was to remove finely crushed rock, sand, rock dust etc., as such material
causes damage if allowed to go through the power house turbines.
August 14 arrived—the day for the river to be turned in at the
intake. A heavy bulkhead had been built across the main tunnel
just below Adit 2, to divert the water and debris into Stevenson
Creek, and thence to the San Joaquin River. John B. Miller, President of the Company, his daughter, Carrita, and some guests, accompanied by George C. Ward, were on hand at the adit portal,
besides local personnel, to see the tunnel given its first bath. The
roar of the water could be heard long before its arrival. All spec-
tators were tense—time passed slowly. Finally, through the adit
rushed the dirtiest river, carrying pieces of broken ties, odds and
ends of lumber, wire, rocks, sand—everything left in the tunnel—
in spite of a previous general clean-up. Mr. Miller, deeply impressed, remarked he had never in all his life witnessed such a
spectacle. After extending congratulations to all of us, he and his
party proceeded to Huntington Lake Lodge to stay over-night,
prior to leaving on their second camping trip in this area.

The following morning, Forest Supervisor M. A. Benedict and
Frank Bonner, District Engineer of the U. S. Forest Service, joined
us at the Lodge to help escort the party to Florence Lake. On the
way, stops were made to inspect the work above Huntington Lake,
and a call was made on Jerry and his dog team. Having enjoyed
a bounteous lunch beneath the pines at Florence Lake, the campers
left by pack train for Blaney Meadows, where a comfortable
camp had been established. Messrs. Ward and Howard accompanied the party, as Mr. Miller wished to have them remain with
him during his ten-day stay.

On Sunday, the 19th, piloted by Mr. Ward, who had returned
to Huntington Lake for the purpose, Mr. Miller had as visitors

Executive Vice President R. H. Ballard, Capt. John Fredericks, Shannon Crandall, H. A. Barre, E. R. Davis and myself. A horse equal to the carrying of Mr. Ballard's substantial size had been provided. On the trip, this particular rider allowed his steed to wander off the trail as he pleased. Much to the surprise of both, they ran into a large hornets' nest. Apparently, all the occupants were at home and vigorously resented being molested. The resulting disturbance through the aspen thickets was proportionate to the size of the nest. There were no more wanderings away from the trail.

Mah Jong, which was sweeping over the country, was a favorite pastime in the Miller camp, and the expert players saw to it that all visiting money remained there. Never do I hear "Parade of the Wooden Soldiers" without being taken back to the delightful atmosphere around those Blaney Meadow camp fires, where I heard it for the first time on Carrita's portable Victrola. She had just returned from school at Dobb's Ferry, and had brought along the record which was then so popular in the east. Carrita loved the mountains—even her dad said so. In later years, as Mrs. Nobles, she returned numerous times, bringing her own children, hoping they would acquire their mother's taste for the big outdoors.

One important feature of pressure tunnels, and, of course, of Tunnel No. 3, is the surge chamber constructed at the lower end. Its chief function is to act as a cushion for the water column. Any surge caused by the sudden shut-down of machines in the power house will be relieved by the water's being allowed to rise and fall in such a chamber. The one under discussion has a shape similar to an hour glass—a large section at the top and bottom, with a smaller-diameter connecting shaft. The reason for such a shape is to permit small and unexpected demands to be taken care of easily by the water available in the enlarged section, without the need for carrying the chamber, full size, all the way to the surface, a distance of two hundred feet. It was located off to the side of the tunnel for construction purposes, since it was easier to proceed with excavation than it would have been had the chamber been placed directly over the tunnel.

At the tunnel outlet, to provide take-off for each of the seven-foot six inch penstocks (three to be for future use) an unusual manifold was located. It consisted of two spheres twenty-four feet in diameter, four penstock outlets from one, and two from the other nearest the tunnel outlet. In the spheres, hoop tension is the force to provide against and this is taken care of by the addition of several steel plate collars around the penstock outlets.

As another part of the No. 3 development, a dam was required in the San Joaquin River gorge for impounding water to be passed through the tunnel for use at the power house. Diamond drill borings were made at three separate sites before a suitable foundation for Dam No. 6 was found. The dam is of simple arch type, having an upstream radius of one hundred and eight feet. The base had a maximum thickness of 37 feet 9 inches, and a spillway crest 8.0 feet in width. Late in 1937, 58,600 second feet of water passed over the dam, the greatest amount the dam has ever discharged. The construction of this dam was about the most difficult job encountered in the development of the entire Big Creek Project. While the dam was being built, the flow of the river had to be carried around the site through a flume hanging on the slick canyon side. A wooden flume was constructed, having a capacity of 5,000 second feet. The size was adopted after careful study of the hydrographic records showed this to be the maximum flow to be expected during the period when diversion would be necessary. Two coffer-dams were required—one at the intake of the flume and the other at the outlet—to keep the excavation in the river bed clear. Fifty six thousand sacks of earth were required for these two coffer-dams, and once during the critical part of excavation, the flume was taxed to the limit. It would have been disastrous had it overflowed and flooded the three shovels working deep below the river bed. We removed a large, water-logged tree, which probably had been covered at such a depth for hundreds of years. It was heavy as lead and in an excellent state of preservation. The excavation was completed on November 15, 1922, and the placing of concrete started on November 20. By December 6 it was possible to abandon the flume, much to the relief of all concerned, and to carry the river through the sluice gates in the bottom of the dam. The placing of concrete was completed on February 8, 1923, except for the closing of the temporary openings above the sluice gates, the last one of which was closed on March 18, just a few days before the first spring flood came down the river.

While the dam was being built, progress was under way on the concrete intake for the tunnel, since it was imperative that it, too, be completed before high water. It is designed to control the flow into the tunnel from the forebay created by Dam No. 6. The structure rises one hundred feet from the lowest point of the foundation, and the control gate is a single cylinder, 22 feet in diameter, and 77½ feet in height. Standing inside this structure at its base, one is reminded—or at least I was, because of its size—of one of the larger movie theaters in Hollywood.

A railroad needs dispatchers to handle its trains, which must go through. A company in the power business needs them to see that the electricity reaches the places where and when it is needed, as it, too, must go through. The dispatchers who control the output of all the Big Creek plants, as well as the allocation of water from the reservoirs, are located in a separate building at Big Creek No. 3, and operate under the Chief System Dispatcher at Alhambra. The dispatcher's load chart, or graphic record, is interesting to study. From it one can see what is happening in the evening as the load decreases—with stores, shops, factories closing, cities going to bed. As early morning activities begin, the increase in load is reflected in the upswing of the graph. In other words, it is possible to observe the comings and goings of cities pretty well from these charts. For instance, at the time of Franklin D. Roosevelt's funeral, a total of 85,000 kilowatts was dropped on the Edison System for one minute.

Much switching is as necessary in the handling of electricity as of trains—but the switches, of course, are of a different type. A large outdoor switching station was built near Big Creek No. 3 Power House. The main transmission lines from all the Big Creek plants are looped into this "switch garden," which consists of many huge switches called "oil circuit breakers" which are operated by remote control from the power house, and other necessary appurtenances. This arrangement is quite flexible—a main line in trouble can be taken out of service, a plant may be isolated, and many situations handled by using various combinations obtainable in the switch garden.

Unit No. 2, the first in the Big Creek No. 3 Plant, went in service on September 30, 1923, at 7:09 P.M., in time to replace the load being supplied to the system from an outside source, the agreement for which expired at midnight. Unit 1 followed on October 2, Unit 3 on the morning of October 5, and the plant was turned over to the Operating Department on October 29.

A most unfortunate accident occurred at the plant on the afternoon of March 14, 1924—the worst ever to happen there. Two men were working on the plunger valve inside the No. 3 penstock, a short distance above the turbine. For some cause unknown to this day, the butterfly valve at the top of the penstock opened, letting in a full head of water. One man was literally blown out the man-hole, unhurt, onto the turbine floor, but the other was forced through the eight inch relief valve opening. The geyser from the penstock man-hole tore through the powerhouse roof about one hundred feet overhead, and attracted the attention of the crew of a passing train on the San Joaquin & Eastern, several miles above.

In May, 1923, a radical departure was made in connection with a practice common to most construction jobs. Prior to that date, men following construction work furnished and carried their own bedding. It was now optional with those on the job whether they continued to do so, or availed themselves of beds furnished by the company. Many, but not all, took advantage of the company bedding; however, it wasn't long until all did so.

At this same time, a program was adopted of showing movies in the various camps at least once a week, and sometimes twice. Another feature which also proved to be popular was boxing bouts. Much talent along this line was found in one camp or another, and it was a common sight during summer to see several hundred men sitting around an outside arena in the evening, watching their favorites in bouts of almost any number of rounds. A referee was always in attendance.

A job such as ours during the '20's was most unusual from any standpoint, and was a mecca for large numbers of salesmen, representing many companies throughout the country. Seldom was there a day when at least one, two, or several did not visit us. We did a large amount of pioneering in the use of various materials and equipment, and close collaboration between salesmen and ourselves resulted in mutual benefit.

XVI

Florence Lake Development

PREPARATIONS

A MAJOR UNDERTAKING, as well as the most conspicuous and spectacular one of the entire Big Creek Project, was the driving of Florence Lake Tunnel.

Preparations on a large scale had to be made. Full advantage had to be taken of the summer months—not only during 1920, the beginning, but through the years until completion of the tunnel. Underground work could proceed, of course, regardless of the weather.

The "60" series of numbers was allocated to the camps which would be constructed for the Florence Lake development. Camp 60, the first, was established for the tunnel outlet at the upper end of Huntington Lake. Men, equipment and material for building the camp were transported that summer by boat and barge across Huntington Lake to Chipmunk Landing. The name was given the place by the men because it appeared to be the favorite hang-out for all Huntington Lake chipmunks. The following year we established a regular landing a short distance to the west, calling it Camp 59.

Horses and mules traveled around the Lake by trail. Late that summer, and as work on the camp progressed, the road over Kaiser Pass was started by our own forces under the direct supervision of Harry M. Allen, general foreman. Men, mules, plows, scrapers, and a donkey engine, constituted the outfit. Although a preliminary survey had been made, the actual location took place as the

99

men, mules and scrapers pushed ahead. The wood-burning donkey engine, with its long reels of cable, pulled itself along and was used to remove boulders, trees, etc., that were too much for the mules.

When it reached Kaiser Pass, at an elevation of 9,305 feet, the black smoke was responsible for much excitement on the part of the Forest Service lookouts. Since there was nothing much to catch fire on the summit, the incident was all the more puzzling until the fire guards learned of the road crew's arrival at that point. Our objective was to reach the Camp 61 site in time to establish a permanent base before winter. It was to be an adit location from which to drive that section of the tunnel towards Huntington Lake. The road crew continued pushing down on the far side of Kaiser Pass, dodging huge boulders and removing many others. Spared wherever possible were the junipers—those sturdy denizens of the High Sierra which have withstood the elements through so many centuries. Though smaller in stature, they are comparable in age to the Sequoia gigantea. The nature of their environment and their general appearance indicate a struggle for existence.

Beyond the Pass about two miles, a scraper exposed some thinly covered fragments of a human skeleton. The mule skinners carefully collected the pieces, fragile from many years of exposure. A large cross, carved on a lodgepole pine, marks the tree at the base of which they were placed.

Temporary "fly" camps were made as the road moved along. Not to cause confusion later with a permanent camp number, they were designated 61-A, B, C, etc.; there being five in all between Camps 60 and 61. The only one retaining its identity today is 61-C, on Kaiser Pass.

Following the road closely was a line crew, cutting and setting native poles for the construction of a 30,000 volt transmission line from Big Creek, since power was one of the most important items to have available as soon as Camp 61 site was reached.

Left: Double jack drillers prepare rock for blasting near Kaiser Pass.

Right: Construction Foreman Harry M. Allen drives the first automobile over Kaiser Pass, Sept. 8, 1920.

Below: Far cry from those used on big construction jobs today were the bulldozers used in the building of the Florence Lake Road in 1920.

Tunnel Foreman Ed McCabe referees a boxing bout at Camp 62 between Jimmie Jessick and Henry Malcor.

Camp 61 base hospital in 1922, duplicate of one destroyed by fire in December, 1921.

In about two months, eleven and one-half miles of fairly good road had been completed, connecting Camps 60 and 61. During the same summer, and as described in a previous chapter, the Government was building, and completed, the present road along the north side of Huntington Lake. Connecting with ours at Camp 60, it completed the length from Big Creek through to Camp 61.

Workmen were busy as bees, constructing facilities not only at Camp 60 but also at Camp 61, now that the road was through. Mess halls, bunkhouses, warehouses, etc., common to both camps, had to be ready before the snow started to fly—and that wasn't far off. Enough supplies had to be provided to see several hundred men through the winter months, as the road would then be closed to ordinary transportation. We built a log cabin on the northerly side of Kaiser Pass, large enough to care for several men if it were necessary for them to remain over-night while passing back and forth between camps. A cook was stationed there to serve meals. Although lumber for the Camp 60 buildings had been taken across Huntington Lake by barge, none could reach Camp 61 until the road was completed—and it was getting late. Shakes were made, which, together with logs and saplings cut nearby, constituted material for beginning construction of enough buildings for the first winter's use until an adequate supply of lumber was available.

Arthur Blight and I showed President Miller, Dr. Bryant, and Mr. Ward over the newly constructed road during Mr. Miller's visit in September, 1920, as far as we could drive by automobile. We took Mr. Ward the two or three remaining miles to Camp 61 by wagon. The other visitors preferred to remain with the cars.

Having taken two months to build the road between Camp 60 and 61, there remained a scant two months more for equipping the latter camp for the winter. At its elevation, 7,100 feet, there are only about six months in the year when the ground is free of snow. The new road which had just been completed around the north side of the lake allowed us to transport supplies by truck from the Lake all the way to both Camps 60 and 61. During the years since there has been a road over Kaiser Pass, we have always hoped to get "just one more job done" before snow called a halt. Especially was that so late in 1920, when Old Man Winter stepped in and closed the road just before Christmas.

Whenever weather permitted, during the first winter at Camp 61, everything possible was accomplished outside. As soon as the road over the Pass was opened in 1921, there were many jobs to be done in the way of further preparation—even at Camp 61. It seemed we never really finished preparations. In fact, up to and including the last year of construction, we were doing things preparatory to completion beyond the Pass. Each camp had to have its own cold storage plant for meat, butter, poultry etc., and they would have done credit to any large packing concern. A central laundry was built and operated at Camp 61, at which attempts were made to handle work for employees, in addition to the Company items. Such efforts were usually accompanied by many headaches, and we were always glad when we could limit orders to Company material, of which there was a great deal. Our experience was much more satisfactory at the large laundry operated at Big Creek headquarters, where women were available as help.

To cut down on distance for hauling lumber, the old sawmill at Shaver was moved and installed near Camp 61 in the summer of 1921. A million board feet did not go far in the midst of so many needs both outside and underground.

A large recreation hall was built at each camp for the movies and all sorts of gatherings. In summer months there were many boxing bouts, which were popular just as at our lower camps. Of course, there was gambling of a sort in spite of attempts to discourage it. The main concern was the fleecing of the men by "card sharks"—the games reaching the nuisance stage.

Mono Base Hospital was built at Camp 61 to serve all camps on that side of Kaiser Pass. Dr. W. N. Carter, formerly located at Kern River No. 3, assumed charge, with Mrs. Carter as head nurse. The large new building had just been completed, and was all in readiness for patients, when, on December 17, 1921, at 5:30 A.M., it caught fire and was completely destroyed. Besides that serious loss, four bunkhouses, the timekeeper's office, the detention ward, and the doctor's residence, suffered damage. It was too late—winter was upon us—to undertake building a new structure. We had to get along with a makeshift arrangement until the following summer, when a duplicate structure was built. First aid stations at the other camps, each in charge of a competent nurse, completed the medical facilities.

Work got under way in the early summer of 1922, to extend the road from Camp 61 to Florence Lake. To expedite completion of the tunnel, it was desirable to have another adit. Camp 62 was chosen as the location—not quite half-way between Camp 61 and Florence Lake. Before adoption of the final location for the present road beyond Camp 61, it was considered advisable to make one more inspection. After a road is once built, it costs money to make changes. A party consisting of Messrs. Ward, Barre, Davis, Dennis, Howard and myself, on horseback, spent an entire day reconnoitering along the ridges to the south high above the road as it is today. The trip was difficult; the steep cliffs we encountered confirmed our judgment on the location already adopted. Numerous places over slick rock were so dangerous to cross that each rider led his horse. During the last crossing, Mr. Ward's horse slipped and slid about fifteen feet, landing upside down at the bottom of a large hole. Slick rock on all sides prevented the animal from getting a foothold; consequently, he couldn't right himself. The poor fellow tried until exhausted, the saddle on his back making it more difficult. We had to wait for a rest period between his efforts, or risk being injured by flying hoofs. Finally, he must have realized the futility of further attempts on his part, and welcomed our assistance. With head, feet and tail holds, we maneuvered the animal into various positions. With the help of all, plus his remaining energy, he was able to turn right side up; fortunately, he was unhurt. It does not take much imagination to picture what the consequences might have been had the rider been aboard. The trip was treacherous in any direction, so we decided to lead our horses down and out as best we could. We came out upon the shore of a lovely pond which we could not identify on any government map. Then and there we named it "Ward Lake" and such it has been since shown upon maps. We built our road along its shore.

By the summer's end, one could drive all the way to the site where Camp 63 was built—the intake for the Florence Lake Tunnel. All facilities previously provided at Camp 61 had to be practically duplicated at the two new camps, 62 and 63, the lumber being cut in the mill then in operation at Camp 61.

XVII

Florence Lake Development

ALASKA DOG TEAM

W E WERE FACED WITH the problem, during winter months, of getting mail and light supplies of various kinds, particularly medicine, over Kaiser Pass with the road impassable on account of deep snow. Equipment for snow removal such as we have today had not been perfected. The decision was made to secure a dog team, the question being how to get one which was trained, with a driver, in time to be of use during the winter which was then upon us. With the assistance of Ingersoll-Rand Company, we obtained a team of seven dogs and a driver from Alaska.

Jerry Dwyer, the dogs, Babe, the leader, Patsy, Dooley, Trim, Riley, Whiskey and Barney, and complete equipment arrived, going into service on December 16, 1920. The team operated between Camp 60, at the upper end of Huntington Lake where it was based, and Camp 61, beyond Kaiser Pass. The normal schedule consisted of a trip over the Pass one day and back the next. During the summer months of the first two years, the team was quartered at Camp 61-C on Kaiser Pass, where it was cooler because of the elevation—9,305 feet.

The dogs received careful attention from Jerry, who cared for them as though they were children. They were fond of fresh fish, especially salmon, which they were fed when it was obtainable.

They always had to be tied and kept far enough apart to prevent their fighting with one another. Along the trail, under some conditions, the snow would cause trouble by balling-up on their feet. To prevent this, Jerry had leather shoes made. The dogs were not too keen about wearing them and when the shoes were put on would jump around for a while as if they were walking over hot coals. Frequently, a trail had to be broken in the deep snow, and this would be accomplished by several men walking ahead, as there were always some traveling back and forth.

Before the first heavy snow, road markers—short wood blocks painted red—were nailed on trees fifteen feet above the ground, and spaced about one hundred yards apart. Where there were no trees, a sapling was cut and set in a mound of rocks along the roadside. These markers were for the guidance of men on foot, as well as for the dog team. It does not take long in these mountains for a blizzard to completely obliterate a road. After nearly thirty years, many of these markers are still in place, arousing the curiosity of visitors.

The dog team had not been working long before it was called into action on an errand of mercy, but too late. An employee located at Camp 61, six miles beyond Kaiser Pass, was determined to get home to spend Christmas with his family in the San Joaquin Valley. Against the advice of his superiors and contemporaries, he reached Camp 61-C on Kaiser Pass, where quarters were available for anyone who might need shelter during storms. After a short stop-over, he insisted on going ahead. It was six and one-half miles to Camp 60, at the upper end of Huntington Lake, and the snow at the Pass was more than waist deep. Three men volunteered to accompany him, not wanting to see him go on alone. The party had not gone far when his exhaustion made it necessary for the others to place their companion at the foot of a large juniper tree— the snow is always light around the bases of large trees—and return

Alaska dog team with Babe in lead.

Jerry Dwyer and his favorite dog,`Babe.

to camp for Jerry and his dogs. When the rescue party finally reached the juniper tree, the man was dead.

Several of our men thought the Alaska dogs should have some competition. Besides, they needed some help as the sled loads were increasing. Seven camp mongrels were pressed into service, to alternate on trips with their more favored competitors. The mongrels presented no problem whatsoever, even though none had ever been harnessed. The new outfit started off like old-timers, and on the first trip the two teams met on Kaiser Pass. It was anticipated there might be trouble, and to prevent this, the teams were kept at a distance in passing. The Alaska dogs paid no particular attention, merely gave a few glances off to the side, as much as to say, "Huh, where did you punks come from?" The mongrel team, however, really had a fit. Each dog growled or snarled, some barked, and the hair on their backs stood straight up; but both teams kept moving. The mongrel team acted in much the same manner each time the other team came in sight during the few weeks, as if saying, "You guys are not so hot."

In September, 1922, Babe, the leader of the Alaskan dogs, died. Jerry buried her on Kaiser Pass, where Whiskey and Trim found a resting place subsequently. Their graves have been marked with an appropriate redwood slab, made and erected by the United States Forest Service. Before the marker was erected there was no identification other than a border of stones around each grave. Since they are alongside the main road, they have become a center of attraction for passing motorists. On numerous occasions I have stopped to join a group—out of curiosity—as it has always been interesting to hear the conjectures. Once when there was only a single grave, one member of such a group, after a long powwow, opined, "Some poor old prospector, I suppose."

After Babe's death, the leadership of the team fell to the black dog, Patsy, a most likable and friendly creature.

Mrs. Redinger extended her sympathy to Jerry, and his reaction to the loss of Babe can be described more easily by quoting his letter to her, written at Camp 61-C on September 20, 1922:

"Dear Mrs. Redinger:

I received your letter this morning and wish to let you know that I am sincerely grateful for your interest and sympathy.

Losing Babe hurt more than I thought possible. For a number of years past I have thought that nothing mattered, but I was mistaken. I consoled myself with the knowledge that I was always good to Babe, and I believe it is better to have her die than to have me leave her. She did not suffer, and died in the arms of the one she loved best in all the world, game to the last. Her last effort was to snuggle up in my arms. That is more than I expect myself when I pass out.

I thank you for the picture. It looks to me a great deal like the picture of Maude Adams in "Joan of Arc"—another great lover of dogs. Her favorite was the dog of all dogs, the Irish wolfhound. I used to know Maude Adams, the angel of the stage, and thought she was the loveliest ever.

With best wishes to you, Mrs. Redinger, I remain

Sincerely,

(Signed)   Jerry Dwyer"

With the above letter he enclosed, in his own handwriting, a copy of that much publicized "A Tribute To The Dog," by Senator George Graham Vest. I do not see how anyone can read it without being deeply touched, causing one, perhaps, to have a more kindly feeling towards man's canine friends. In addition, Jerry also sent, in further tribute to Babe, a poem which had been sent to him, written by G. F. Rinehart, who, at that time, was editor of the "Covina Citizen." This is the poem:

On the topmost reach of the Kaiser Crest
Where the clouds commune and weep,
In a granite tomb 'til the crack of doom,
Babe lies in her last long sleep.

Though born to the law of the tooth and fang
In the land of Alaskan Snow
Of the Savage pack that follows the track
In blood-lust for its foe.

The Wolf-Dog shatters genetic law
That each seeks kith or clan
For the Wolf-Dog mind will forsake its kind
To become the friend of Man.

At the word of command from her Friend and Pal
Past pinnacle, spire and dome
Through the blizzard's blast she was sure and fast
To mush with the mail from home.

For thirty miles to the snow bound lake
She was always willing to go
On a dangerous trail, with the daily mail
To the men marooned in snow.

When the Tourist conquers the tortuous steeps
With the Kaiser Pass as his goal
He will pause and rest on the wind-swept Crest
Where lies this Dog with a soul.

The author, during visits to the Lodge and area at previous times, had become acquainted with Jerry and his dogs.

As he indicated in his letter, Jerry had thought of his leaving

Babe at some future time, also of his feeling prior to Babe's death that nothing mattered insofar as he himself was concerned. He never talked much about himself, his principal interest being his dogs—at least, during the several years he was here. We never knew much about his past, as there was never any inclination on his part to discuss it. He and his dog team received wide publicity and accomplished much in their line of work, especially during emergencies in storms. An inquiry came to me from Hartford, Connecticut, the writer being the editor of the "Hartford Courant." By indirect questioning, all that could be learned was that Jerry was familiar with that part of the country. The Hartford editor replied, appreciating the information—even though meager—stating that Jerry came from a high-ranking New England family.

Jerry liked Mrs. Redinger, probably because she displayed interest in him and his dogs. When he left here in 1927, he told her that he would send her a card from time to time but that she would never find any address on it. That proved to be the case with several which she did receive. The last one, received in 1931, was postmarked "Seattle, Washington," and nothing is known as to what happened to him after that date.

XVIII

Florence Lake Development

RADIO COMMUNICATION

ONE OF THE MOST IMPORTANT factors of any construction job is a means of quick and dependable communication. We realized the uncertainty of reliable service from a telephone line over Kaiser Pass and besides, maintenance would be expensive. Previously, the Edison Company had used satisfactorily a telegraph circuit between Los Angeles and the Kern River No. 3 project. A similar hook-up had already been made between Los Angeles and Big Creek.

It was decided to make some tests in the Big Creek area as to the practicability of radio-telegraph for the upper camps. The late Messrs. Roy Ashbrook and Ralph Henry were encouraged sufficiently by the tests to proceed with the installation of such communication between Big Creek and all the upper camps to be established. Ashbrook was furnished a small, pine, slab-covered structure about eight by ten feet, from which he made the necessary tests at the Big Creek end. After it had served its purpose, I had it moved into my back yard. Called "the little brown house," it has continued through the years to render valuable service, sometimes as guests' quarters.

What with the telephone and telegraph circuits to Los Angeles, supplemented by the radio, communication traffic was seen as a major item of the construction program; consequently, we constructed a special building here at headquarters to accommodate the facilities and operators, there being three shifts—telephone and radio—on duty during the heavy construction years.

Radio operations really started in November, 1920. Enroute to Camp 61 on foot early in 1922, I heard my first radio broadcast. While lying on a cot in the attic of Camp 61-C's log cabin overnight, I listened with headphones to an alumni address by Dr. Suzzalo, President of the University of Washington. In those years, the Camp 61-C radio station was reported to be the highest in the world.

Knowing my interest in radio, Operator "Red" Fordham would always hand me items of interest whenever I stopped at his station. I recall several messages passing between Ashbrook and Henry, in which Ashbrook was trying to locate his "Church Warden." As I was not familiar with the name, and since there were no churches in the vicinity, my curiosity was aroused—hence, my message, "What is all this church warden stuff?" Had I recalled James Whitcomb Riley's "That Old Sweetheart of Mine," I would have known it was also Ashbrook's favorite smoking tobacco.

The communication traffic flourished, especially via radio and telegraph circuits. Our reports indicated that for the month of November, 1923, more than a half-million words were handled. By that time the service had been extended to Camp 63 at Florence Lake.

A letter was received from a man in Idaho. Being an amateur, he had been picking up some of our messages and was concerned about a special type of bolt a camp foreman was having trouble locating. He offered to send down one he happened to have.

The operators at Big Creek Headquarters were discussing the possibility of reaching the Redingers who were in Japan on a trip in the Orient. They decided to try, and their message, picked up by an amateur in Shanghai, was received by mail at Kobe. The

$10.00 for the three word acknowledgment by cable was considered well spent.

Milton Kempt, foreman at Camp 61, in sending radio messages to Big Creek Headquarters, always ended with the words, "Everything else O.K.," regardless of the contents. As we went aboard ship at Honolulu to continue across the Pacific after a two weeks' stopover, I found in my mail a message from Big Creek sent by George C. Heckman which was a take-off on those by Kempt. Typewritten on the standard form used for radio was the following:

CAMP 61C, JANUARY 15, 1927.

SNOWING HARD STOP SNOW ON LEVEL TWELVE FEET STOP DOG TEAM COMING UP FROM CAMP SIXTY WITH FRESH FISH AND ORANGES FOR THE MEN ISOLATED IN THE CAMPS STOP TRUCK NO. 1313 LOST ITS ENGINE BETWEEN CAMP 60 AND CAMP 61C. THIS WAS NOT NOTICED UNTIL TRUCK ARRIVED. SHALL WE SEND THE DOG TEAM BACK TO LOOK FOR THE ENGINE STOP THE ROSES AND CARNATIONS DID NOT ARRIVE ON THE TRUCK. THOUGHT THE COOK AT CAMP 60 MIGHT HAVE MADE A MISTAKE AND USED THEM FOR SALAD. PLEASE ADVISE STOP HAVE FOUND ONLY ONE POTATO FROZEN OUT OF THE TEN MILLION STOP CARETAKER AT CAMP 63 TURNING THE EGGS OVER FINDS THERE A MILLION OR MORE AND WILL TAKE HIM SEVERAL YEARS TO DO THE JOB HOWEVER HAVE ADVISED HIM NOT TO TURN ONE AT A TIME BUT ONE CRATE INSTEAD. THIS METHOD WILL TAKE ONLY A FEW HOURS STOP THE ELECTRIC LOCOMOTIVES ARE STILL LOCO STOP HECKMAN, PESTERFIELD AND THE GOODWILL MAN JUST LEFT HERE IN A BOB SLED FOR A VISIT TO THE OTHER CAMPS. EVERYTHING ELSE O. K.

(SIGNED) CAMP FOREMAN

The radio operators were able to keep the various camps quite well posted on current news items gleaned from various sources, and the men looked forward each day to such information.

As far as is known, our radio-telegraph was the first to be used on such a large construction job. It was very satisfactory through the years—most of the '20's—that it served the upper camps. Today, at Florence Lake we are using as a mess hall the steel building which formerly served as the radio building. It is still referred to and better known as "the old radio shack." Here at Big Creek, Boy Scouts make use of the tile-roofed concrete structure which for years was the headquarters for all our heavy telephone, telegraph and radio traffic.

MESSAGE RECEIVED   ARRL.

'81 Avenue dubail, Shanghai.

VIA AMATER RADIO   AC-1CRS.

From 6CQ via OP-1HR   No. 1   No. of words   date and Time handed in Feb 12   *1927* M

Service Instructions Mail dlvy   Date and time rcvd. Feb 16 7.40p   M   By

To   D.H. Redinger. Oriental Hotel Kobe Japan.

Greetings and best wishes for a pleasant trip herewith sent by radio from Big Creek amateur station -

Sign:- Big Creek, Construction Dept.

With Compliments

R SHEKURY

XIX

Florence Lake Tunnel

QUARTERS FOR THE WINTER had been made ready at Camp 60, the tunnel outlet, by October. The big job for which there had been so much preparation was ready to be tackled. The distance through the mountain beneath Kaiser Pass to Camp 61 is six and one-half miles, and it was a mammoth undertaking to blast a hole that length, in hard granite most of the way. Tunnel men refer to any kind of material as "ground."

A short open cut to establish the outlet portal was necessary. This done, the first set of timbers was placed on October 15, 1920, marking the start to go underground.

A big factor to be expected in most tunnel work is water. It constitutes a problem by itself, and conditions are aggravated if boulders, sand and mud are encountered with it. To start with, we struck all four at the outlet. Progress was slow the first winter. Much timbering was required, and hand labor was all that could be used. The open cut to the adit portal at Camp 61 was started in November, the same year. Progress underground was also slow and discouraging, due to running sand, always difficult to handle. Many bales of straw were stuffed behind the timbers to combat the sand effectively.

By April, 1921, the adit was less than one-third the distance to the point where tunnel driving could start towards Camp 60 and Florence Lake. A glance at the progress chart was sufficient to realize the seriousness of the situation, in looking ahead to final completion and ultimate expenditures. The decision was made to sink a shaft to the main tunnel grade west of the adit, towards Camp 60, to speed progress. Started on April 15, it was finished to tunnel grade on July 23, a depth of 247 feet through hard granite.

Excavation started at once on the tunnel, one crew working toward the outlet, six miles away, the other toward the Camp 61 adit intersection.

To speed up excavation still further, another shaft was started on June 25, the same year, near the Camp 61 adit intersection, to permit driving towards the adit portal and also towards the first shaft. Of great importance was the completion of this adit which allowed the muck trains to operate over a level grade to and from the tunnel. The 87-foot depth to tunnel grade, through very hard granite, was completed in forty-nine days—very good progress for a large two-compartment shaft.

By the middle of February, 1922, the adit was completed, and the muck trains could operate to and from the outside. On April 6, the section of tunnel between the two shafts holed through, and the total progress at Camp 61 amounted to 2,900 feet of main tunnel in addition to the 1,086 feet of adit. In the meantime, more than half a mile had been driven at Camp 60. Things were now set for straight-away tunnel driving from both Camps 60 and 61—the long section, the one towards the outlet at Camp 60, where efforts were now concentrated.

A natural question that has been asked frequently is, "Why were two angles made in the tunnel, thereby increasing its length?" A straight tunnel would have been two miles shorter. The longer one could be driven in two years' less time because it allowed two adits, whereas the topography on a straight line would not. Each adit provided two more headings, or working faces, a total of six including the intake and outlet. On a straight line there would have been only two. However, shafts on a straight line tunnel would have been impractical because of the great depth.

Special size steam shovel used in construction of Florence Lake Tunnel.

A few of the fleet of Mack trucks on the way up Kaiser Pass with supplies for the Florence Lake project.

*Above: This building
accommodated
C. P. Staal's accounting
department, and
resident engineer's office
was in building at
left, rear.*

*Left: One day's
mail at Big Creek near
Christmastime.*

By the latter part of 1922, Adit Camp 62 had been established as had been Camp 63 at the intake portal. The job had reached a stage at which close supervision was required, and Herman Kruger assumed direct charge through to completion, after which time he became general superintendent on field construction. Equipment to suit the 15 foot by 15 foot tunnel was provided, and with better organization all around, we looked forward to improvement in progress.

Tunnel crews commenced to vie with one another in making footage. Three eight-hour shifts seemed to work best. The small Armstrong "Shoveloders" were replaced with special Marion steam shovels, operated by compressed air. Combination storage battery and trolley locomotives, Baldwin-Westinghouse, eight-ton type, hauled trains of muck cars of four to six cubic feet capacity. The trolley was used to within eight hundred to one thousand feet of a heading, after which the storage battery took over. The trolley could not go closer, as it would be shot down or damaged each time a round of holes was fired.

Our payroll and the number of camps were not the only things increasing rapidly with the expanding program along the sixty-mile front from Auberry to Camp 63. Uptown Big Creek was enjoying a boom during the '20's, such as it never knew before or has known since. Our five-thousand to fifty-two hundred men, spread over thirty-two camps, kept three barber shops and six dentists busy. In the larger camps, especially those isolated in winter, there was always those amongst the employees with enough barber experience to cater to tonsorial needs until summer. Reardon's movie theater provided good films and current news reels. Busiest of all was Murphy's Art Shop. If he didn't have what you wanted, he would order it—whether it was a penny article or a grand piano. "Murphy's Art Shop News," printed by him and distributed free of charge over the project, served as an excellent advertising medium, besides carrying local items of interest. The unique publication attracted attention far and near. W. L. Murphy came to Big Creek as a stenographer for R. V. Haslett, our storekeeper. He recognized and took advantage of an opportunity which would have proved even more profitable if fire had not destroyed the enterprise in 1930.

During all the years of construction, the Florence Lake road above Camp 60 was closed to the general public in summer months. The gate between the upper end of Huntington Lake and Camp 60 was attended twenty-four hours a day, entrance being restricted to Edison Company and U. S. Forest Service vehicles. It took something most extraordinary to justify a special pass. This restriction was necessary because travel by the general public would have seriously interfered with the operation of all equipment, to say nothing of endangering the cars of campers, sight-seers, fishermen etc. No restriction was placed on hikers or horseback riders, of which there were few. Because of our heavy traffic and in order to keep the road in good condition, we kept the road wet with tank sprinklers which worked at night, when evaporation and travel were less. Today we would probably use oil.

The results we were getting elsewhere with the faster and more powerful Ingersoll-Rand X-70 rock drills—or "machines," as the men called them—justified their use in the Florence Lake Tunnel, so we replaced the lighter and smaller 248's with them.

Good ventilation must be provided in tunnel work. We started with a positive type of blower, Root No. 3, but as the working faces were pushed ahead, we naturally required more capacity. The smaller blowers were replaced with the larger Root No. 7, which was ample for distances varying from 11,000 to 12,000 feet. Beyond that distance another one would be installed along the 24-inch ventilation pipe line to act as a booster, in the same capacity as a booster pump in a large oil line. Woodstave pipe had two advantages over iron; less chance of collapse from blasting concussion, and, if a rock fragment punched a hole, it could readily be patched, whereas iron pipe, if crushed, requires renewal of the section. In spite of these advantages of woodstave pipe, we found after two years it had become unsatisfactory, having dried and shrunk from the air and powder smoke passing through, and extensive maintenance was necessary, such as putting on bands to squeeze the staves together. Tests with 24-inch corrugated iron pipe proved quite satisfactory, provided a smooth liner was placed inside to reduce friction caused by the corrugation. The ventilating, or blower pipe was carried along near the roof and kept within about three hundred feet of a working face. This allowed more space along the tunnel wall on the floor for storing various kinds of material. Another advantage of this practice was that it was easier to remove gases generated from blasting, which ordinarily rise. After a round was fired, the blowers would be reversed to withdraw the powder smoke. To assist in clearing the heading as quickly as possible, it was found effective to use an air curtain. Perforated one-inch pipe was laid transversely to the tunnel, on the floor, a short distance toward the portal from the end of the 24-inch blower pipe. The last man to leave the heading before the round was fired would open the air valve feeding the one-inch pipe. The released air, directed towards the roof, would retard the smoke until it was withdrawn by the blower. Somewhat more effective was the use of a water spray instead of air. No one was allowed to return to the heading until a half-hour after blasting; this was a safety measure against delayed holes. The heading and bench method was used in driving, the blasting being done electrically from a 440 volt circuit. The various powder companies endeavored to provide a product that would generate the smallest amount of objectionable gases, and means to that end was a special kind of paper wrapper. Much improvement was made in that respect with the explosives then used exclusively, 40-60 percent gelatin powder, known to the layman as "dynamite."

Our hog business was extended to Camp 61, where it thrived as it had in locations below Big Creek. We did have some havoc caused by such diseases as cholera. One of the tenders at Camp 61 was a character. He admitted frankly that he had known nothing about shoes until he reached the age of twenty—so why should he be bothered with sox, which had to be changed every two or three weeks? The garbage was hauled in the camp "candy" wagon, and this tender attracted attention because of a wash tub in front of the seat, in which he always kept his feet when he was driving. The men's curiosity was satisfied only when they learned he was keeping his feet warm on cool mornings by submerging them in left-over cooked cereal, still warm. He was forced to occupy isolated quarters, as the men objected to his brand of "perfume," which was anything but "My Sin" or "Chanel No. 5."

A winter spent in any of the Florence Lake camps was an excellent way for a man to accumulate a good stake. Some made good use of their savings; others, when they went out for a time, did not fare too well. I recall one who had twenty-five pay checks in his pocket, and who was back at work, broke, within ten days. In Fresno the train would be met by men waiting for "live ones" from Big Creek, who were ready and willing to help relieve the workers of their "wads" across the tracks. It did not take long to get "rolled" or "hi-jacked" in various other places. Back they would come for another "sentence," as some termed it.

Many times I have wondered how many millions of Big Creek dollars were spent through the years in Fresno alone. During the big years, the Edison Company maintained offices in Fresno. Fred Henry, as purchasing agent, kept R. V. Haslett busy at the Big Creek end, and vice versa, both handling millions of dollars worth of material and equipment. The Los Angeles Office was in there "pitching" also. George Campbell, in Fresno, kept the men coming. The accounting department at Big Creek, under the field super-vision of C. R. Duncan, representing C. P. Staal, was kept busy, too.

Not only did invoices have to be paid, but there were pay days for the thousands of employees, who were divided into three groups— one working, one coming and one going. Those days we could give jobs to all comers.

As soon as the road over Kaiser Pass was open each spring, every- one would go all out during the summer to stock the upper camps for another winter. One of the major items of food for any camp was fresh meat. There were about 2000 men in the Florence Lake Camps when all six tunnel headings were being worked. During the four and one-half years of tunnel construction, two million pounds of fresh meat were consumed, and served with it were 1,770,000 pounds of potatoes. The latter, some of the finest in the land, were bought several carloads at a time. Fred Henry would send a man to Idaho into the field while the crop was being har- vested. Such spuds! The Northern Pacific and the Great Northern dining cars featuring those tubers had nothing on the camps. An ideal arrangement was made with a local cattle man to supply our meat and deliver it to each cold storage plant. The cattle would be driven into the back country as early as the season would allow, grazing under a Forest Service permit until fall, when they were slaughtered nearby. The rows upon rows of halves of choicest beef hanging in each plant would have given Paul Bunyan a thrill. Mr. Ward, Vice-President of the Edison Company in charge of all construction and operation, was a connoisseur who, on his many visits, never missed an opportunity to look in on the sight that would have made an avowed vegetarian drool. What's more, we always saw to it that he enjoyed a choice cut at any of the upper camps. He was an early riser and liked to leave Big Creek early enough to have breakfast at Camp 61-C, where we had a chef re- nowned for his golden brown hot cakes, the size of a breakfast plate and really "out of this world."

On numerous occasions Mr. Ward had discussed the Kaiser

Crest junipers, in which he displayed unusual interest, especially when observing them in their habitat. On one trip, he and a guest, also interested in trees, stopped to study closely one we could not dodge when building the road. During luncheon at Camp 61, comments were made about the age of the grizzled monarchs, the conclusion being there was no question but that they were at least twenty-five hundred years old. The conversation, carried on extensively, attracted the attention of several tunnel men at an adjoining table, who listened in silence. On my next trip to the camp one of the timekeepers, reminding me of the previous discussion, related what took place after we had left. The tunnel men took up the subject, and reached some conclusions themselves—at least one did. He remarked, "You fellows can let those guys stuff that kind of bunk down your necks, but they can't make me believe anything like those trees being two or three thousand years old. Hell, this is only 1922 now."

A sizable job was the proper coordination of the numerous mess halls, meals, proper supplies, help etc. A. F. McCarthy, chief steward of the upper camps, did not find time heavy on his hands. Neither did C. A. McDonald, who supervised the Big Creek headquarters camp along with some others. Under each were chief cooks, day cooks, night cooks, bakers, waiters ("flunkies" in construction) vegetable men, dishwashers, and roust-abouts. A mess hall crew "raised hob" occasionally when they tapped a keg of home brew which had been "working" beneath the kitchen floor or in an obscure closet. Sometimes such festivities would be delayed when the thing blew up without warning. Eternal vigilance by the chief steward did not prevent such occurrences. It was no cure to discharge the culprits and get a new gang; everything would be serene for a while, then would usually end in a blow-up, again disrupting the meal situation temporarily.

"Daddy" Grabner was head baker at Big Creek headquarters,

Underground mess hall one to three miles from portal.

Big Creek headquarters mess hall.

Mr. Ward, right, and Mr. Davis chat with author in latter's office at Big Creek.

Job personnel at last break-through, left to right, Sandy Gilzean, Floyd Huntington, author, H. A. Kruger, Ed McCabe, E. C. Panton, Deafy Huntington, Jack Lamy, E. R. Davis, A. F. Blight and R. C. Booth.

where a huge bakery was operated for years. The upper camps had to do their own baking, especially during the winters. When the whole project was going full blast, a month's consumption required 55,000 loaves of bread, 5,000 cakes and 36,000 pies. Mess halls—the larger ones, of course—were operating around the clock.

As the Florence Lake tunnel headings in the longer sections progressed, they were so far underground that it was impracticable to transport the men in and out for meals. To do so would have taken about two hours for a three to six-mile round trip. For the mid-shift meal, a unique dining car service was established, which took the food to the men and served it near the heading. These trains consisted of five electric-lighted flat cars—three equipped with tables and benches, the other two with racks holding the food in hot containers. Help from the mess hall served as if it were a regular dining room. One of those underground meals was a novel experience, and I do not recall ever hearing a complaint. It was very much more comfortable inside than out, cool in summer and warm in winter.

For several summers we operated courtesy cars, taking as guests people who were interested in seeing the work being done in the back country. Regular schedules starting from the Lodge accommodated hundreds. Special groups were handled in large buses, like those used to transport our men to and from the upper camps. One particular party sponsored by the Edison Company was being escorted by D. A. Munger, the usual genial host on such occasions. Having been shown over the Florence Lake work, the guests were returning to the Lodge, when from the black smoke darkening the sky it was evident that there was a bad forest fire some miles distant. The grave consequences of such fires were purposely called to the guests' attention, for reasons shortly to become obvious. The subject under discussion, according to hurriedly made plans unknown to Munger, was that forest rangers, in dire need of fire fighters, can commandeer anyone in the vicinity. By the time the group had conceived such a possibility in its own case, the buses reached the gate at Camp 60. Two rangers "happened" to be with the gate attendant. Approaching the buses, they proceeded to enlighten the occupants further, stressing the seriousness of the fire and the urgent need for help. Herb Barre, Executive Engineer of the Edison Company—good at playing pranks, and one of the instigators of the plot—was accompanying the party. He was chuckling to himself at the expense of the innocent visitors, some of whom were now literally shaking in their shoes. All kinds of excuses were made to the rangers—important business engagements elsewhere, no suitable clothes or shoes, poor physical condition, even such excuses as heart ailments. By this time Barre was about to explode, and Munger, for once, was at his wit's end. The situation was tense for a long five minutes while Munger was looking for me, being sure I knew the rangers. Pretending innocence, I had difficulty maintaining a straight face. He came running, and asked frantically, "Dave, for God's sake, can't you call off the dogs? These men are in no condition to fight fires etc." Someone "in the know" giggled at this most opportune time and the jig was up. That evening relief was evident in the guests' unusually high spirits and good humor as they sat around the fireplace in the Lodge lobby.

As the tunnel was pushed ahead, we ran into bad ground from time to time. Such places always retard progress. The worst condition was encountered where we least expected to find it—beneath Kaiser Meadow, which is close to Kaiser Pass. The half-mile depth of cover is greater there than anywhere else along the tunnel. Extra heavy timbers, closely spaced, were required to hold the "swelling ground"—boulders, broken rock, sand, mud and much water—we had all these for several hundred feet. Water is a problem any time. Pumping is required when the water is on the wrong side of a heading and can not drain out. The slope, or grade, of the tunnel is about three feet in one thousand. We flattened it for several hundred feet in one section to ease the water difficulties. An eminent geologist on the staff of the U. S. Geological Survey, Francois E. Matthes, displayed great interest in our tunnel excavation. He had studied the formations of the Grand Canyon and Yosemite Valley. I spent considerable time with him beneath Kaiser Meadow, while he was making observations. To explain the "swelling ground" in such a location, he applied the geological term "roof pendant," a former canyon filled during the Glacial Age with the material we encountered. When the bad section was concreted later, the heaviest reinforcement in the tunnel was provided in the form of steel rails placed close together, supplementing the regular reinforcing bars.

Each camp had to be self-sustaining in practically all respects. Each had its own compressor plant to furnish the large amounts of compressed air required for the respective tunnel headings. A machine shop, sufficient for mechanical maintenance, was busy continuously. Machine "doctors" for keeping their X-70 "patients" in drilling condition had their work benches inside the tunnel and out. Day and night the heavy thump of the pneumatic drill sharpeners could be heard, as if they were playing bass to the pound of the huge compressors before the pressure was relieved by the unloader valves. "Nippers" shuttled in and out of the tunnel, bringing drill steel to be sharpened, and hurrying back with a load ready to go into the machines at the heading. The miles of track required the continuous attention of maintenance crews, or "gandy dancers," as they are called today.

We experimented at Camp 60 with the first detachable bit for hard-rock drilling. Being something new, it did not take with the tunnel men. Today, an improved bit in all sizes and shapes is used universally. However, tunnel men on large jobs where much steel is used prefer the orthodox type with the bit an integral part of the drill steel.

Electricians were "on the go" like everyone else, the electric locomotives requiring not only their attention but also that of mechanics. Storage batteries were on the racks continuously, especially for re-charging. Our electric railway system was rather unique, although its use was not peculiar to the Florence Lake Tunnel. Ours had, for safety in operation, quite an elaborate, but not complicated block signal system. Extra precautions were necessary where long stretches of single track were involved. Tunnels are usually more or less smoky or hazy. Switches were operated automatically, with red lights indicating on-coming trains, and white, a clear track.

Somewhat electrical-minded myself, I wanted to satisfy a desire to observe a real electric locomotive at work. Thanks to D. A. Munger, Edison Company traffic manager, I was able to ride over a division in a huge one, pulling the "Olympian" of the Chicago, Milwaukee and St. Paul on a trip east. Without a bobble or an indication of wanting to catch its breath, the giant pulled a long train through the Cascades and headed for the wide open spaces like a race horse given full rein after having been held back. The cab was spic and span; there was no coal or oil to cause smoke. Seated behind the engineer, I felt as if I were enjoying a ride in a parlor car. His hair being white, I assumed he had had a steam locomotive previously, and inquired how he liked the electric in comparison. His face lighted up, and with no desire to cast any reflection on his first love, he explained the difference. When something went wrong with the steam locomotive only a few minutes were necessary to locate the trouble but all day to fix it; whereas, it took all day to find trouble in the electric, and only a few minutes to fix it.

The upper camps enjoyed the services of the County Library, supervised by Lila Lofberg, who subsequently wrote a book of her own, "Sierra Outpost," in which she gives an excellent picture of the unusual experiences of herself and her husband, Ted, during the nine years they lived the year 'round at Florence Lake.

Any description of our tunnel work would not be complete without something about Milton Kempt, the camp foreman who always ended his radio messages, "Everything else O. K." He had added the "t" to his surname because he thought there were "too damn many people as Kemp." Often referred to as a "human mole," he had spent his thirty years underground in every large tunnel in the western hemisphere. He was a large man and a hard worker— it seemed as if he were always in the tunnel. His command of "cuss" words on occasion would have shocked Ingersoll, but a man more tender-hearted and kind never lived. His one objective was tunnel progress, and he did not spare himself to achieve it. Previously, he had been engaged on the Edison Company's Kern River No. 3 Project. Occasionally, he rendered a discourse on the stage of degradation reached by any man who would wear a wrist watch, so Harry Dennis not only presented him with one at a mess hall dinner in his honor, but actually put it on his wrist. His contemporaries, asking the time of day, made life miserable for him until the novelty wore off. Kempt was a confirmed bachelor—or so we thought, until he fell for an attractive lady known to many of us. He would not return to camp with her, but preferred to return alone, planning to have her follow shortly. The "reception committee" took care of him when he arrived by train at Big Creek. He was given a ride in the bottom of a dump wagon, which stopped in front of the main office. Before the crowd, the driver released the trip, dumping the bridegroom through the bottom onto the ground, much to his embarrassment. The joke might have had serious consequences had the mules taken a notion to run at that moment. On trips to Camp 61, after he had forsaken bachelor quarters, I enjoyed the hospitality of his home. Always, as soon as the evening meal was over, he would have something out in camp or in the tunnel to show me. After one experience I knew the reason and expected such an invitation. He had been for too many years a devotee of "Lady Nicotine," which was objectionable to his wife in the form

he used it—chewing—and how! He could not get out of the house
fast enough. We always visited the tunnel because of the special
cache where he kept his "chawin'." Several times on the way out,
I had to remind him to remove the eight to ten-inch plug sticking
out of his hip pocket. Such a reminder would be an excuse for biting
off a hunk big enough to last until he made a return trip.

An item that received special attention, and was common to the
upper camp commissary particularly, was "snoose." To have allowed the supply to run out would have caused worse repercussions
than would dynamite. A "snoose eater" will turn Heaven and earth
upside down if he runs out and finds none on hand. The black
stuff is removed from around the inside edge of the small circular
cardboard box by a simple twist of the forefinger. The ultimate
in the art of its use has been reached when the proper amount for
a good gob can be judged and tenderly placed between the cheek
and lower gums.

The transportation of material and supplies to the upper camps
during the summer months for the following winter was always
a big job for many, especially the transportation department. As
many as twenty-five large dump trucks at a time were hauling
between Camp 10, near the top of the main incline to Huntington
Lake, and the camps. Grover Blades kept the fleet moving in both
directions, besides looking after vehicles traveling here, there, and
elsewhere.

There was so much mail we had to establish our own facilities
for handling it after we received it from the local U. S. Postoffice.
During the years, 1923, '24 and '25 alone, we received a total of
1,463,352 pounds by actual weight. During the same period, there
was a total of 168,879 pieces of registered and insured mail handled,
without the loss of a single one.

Edison Company's Vice-President and General Manager, R. H.
Ballard, paid us an occasional visit. He might accompany some

special group from Los Angeles, in which case, he would usually address them during the evening in the Huntington Lodge lobby, giving a general description of the development under way, and its magnitude. On one occasion, telling about the Florence Lake tunnel, he referred to the crews, two or three years hence, looking for each other deep beneath Kaiser Pass. Herb Barre, sitting next to me in a far corner, leaned over at that moment and said, "Dave, there'll certainly be Hell to pay if they don't find each other."

It was always a thrill, especially for tunnel crews that had been working towards each other for several years, when the first faintest "peck-peck" of the drills was heard in the opposite heading. The sound, of course, increases gradually as the distance between headings decreases. In hard rock the sound can be heard for a long distance. The harder the rock, the farther it carries.

We were using an enormous amount of powder. I recall one order for thirty-two carloads. During the period from 1921 to 1925, inclusive, for the entire Big Creek project, we used twelve million pounds—which would have filled two hundred flat cars. Had the sticks been placed end to end, they would have extended from the Edison Building in Los Angeles to the Hawaiian Islands. Although in most of our tunnel shooting the exploders were detonated from an electric circuit, there were many uses for fuse. The 5,750,000 feet in one piece would have been over one thousand miles long, and if ignited would have required ten years for the spark to travel from one end to the other.

Besides the food supplies consumed in the mess halls, there was food purchased for resale to the hundreds of families scattered over many camps. During the five-year period previously mentioned, 12,750,000 pounds of ham and bacon were purchased. The 11,100,000 eggs, if distributed among the people of Los Angeles at that time, would have provided each person with not less than one dozen. The food purchased for the mess halls alone, during the period, would have sustained one thousand people for fourteen years. Items of special interest today are the 36,750 bales of hay and 33,500 sacks of barley for horses and mules, enough to feed one hundred head for ten years. The 25,000,000 board feet of lumber, with the 1,000,000 pounds of nails, were sufficient to build four thousand Southern California five-room bungalows, with enough left over for a fence around each.

It is not unusual for someone to ask, because of the name, if all the Edison Companies in the country are under the same management. The only connection is in the name "Edison," which is symbolic of electricity. This reminds me of the man employed at Camp 61 who had something on his mind. He addressed a letter to "Thomas A. Edison" stating that he was a firm believer in always taking unusual matters up with the "top management." He certainly went all-out in this case. The letter, making the rounds, must have been the source of many chuckles in the various Edison plants and offices, judging from the initials, comments etc., when it finally found its way to Big Creek, having been forwarded from New Jersey.

The "break-through," awaited with utmost anxiety as its time drew near, was the last one in the stretch between Camp 62 and the upper portal. Everyone watched the progress charts, from which the time could be estimated closely. During the early part of the night of February 18, 1925, it happened. The last shot was fired, and a number of us in addition to the crews were on hand to peer through the hole which completed the tunnel excavation nearly two years ahead of schedule. For such a hard-rock tunnel, and for those days, some excellent progress had been made: 30 feet in one day, 174 feet in one week, and 692 feet in one month. Being the longest water tunnel of its size ever constructed up to that time, it was famous among the big tunnels of the world.

Before the track was removed, full advantage was taken of the opportunity to haul material all the way through from Huntington

Lake. Going through Kaiser Crest instead of over was indeed a new experience for all of us, besides expediting the start of construction on the Florence Lake Dam.

To permit stream diversion to the tunnel, and to serve as a cofferdam during construction of the big dam, a low timber-crib dam, rock-filled, was built several hundred feet upstream. The permanent intake for regulating the flow into the tunnel consists of two cylinder gates, each six feet in diameter and about one hundred feet long, placed in an open shaft five hundred feet downstream from the upper portal—freedom from ice being an important factor in selecting the location and type of structure.

The first water release through the tunnel is officially recorded as having taken place on April 13, 1925. In passing through, the water drops 220 feet from the floor of the upper portal to the outlet, fifty feet above the high water level of Huntington Lake. The total natural seepage into the tunnel throughout its length was five cubic feet per second at the time it was placed in service. About ten per cent of its length is lined with concrete, most of which was placed concurrently with tunnel excavation.

The enormous amount of material and equipment placed in the tunnel during the four and one-half years of construction was in direct contrast to the short time required for its removal after the last round was fired. Regardless of how interesting a big job may have been, men usually delight in tearing down and clearing out everything they have built up for purposes of construction. One reason, perhaps, is the excitement created by that "extra burst of speed" as the main job is finished.

There was much concern about possible under-cutting due to back-lash of the water discharging at the tunnel outlet, which is surrounded by a deep layer of glacial-like material. To determine what the action would be, we built a lumber flume about 1,000 feet in length to discharge onto a rail mat near the high water line of Huntington Lake. Observations over a period of two years, with flows as high as 2,300 second feet, were such as to justify the flume's abandonment and subsequent replacement with the present three hundred feet of twelve-foot diameter riveted pipe on a steeper grade, sealed into the tunnel outlet. The water, rushing madly as it leaves the big pipe, quickly made its own pool, with no tendency to encroach beyond the banks. The pool, which is twenty to twenty-five feet deep and one hundred feet across, is a favorite spot for trout which wander upstream from the lake. Depending upon the amount of water coming through the tunnel, its velocity as it leaves the large pipe may be as high as forty to fifty feet per second, knocking the trout end over end in their attempts to move upstream through it.

Day and night, month after month, year after year, the electric locomotives rolled out their trains of muck cars to be dumped on the ever-widening "spoil" banks along the hillside in front of each tunnel and adit portal. Long snow sheds kept the main entrance tracks clear in winter. Several hundred thousand cubic yards of broken granite will long remain as silent markers of the former camps where men labored, not only for their livelihood, but to help provide more electric power for the comfort and progress of humanity.

Mr. Ward became president of the Company in 1932, and served as such until his death in 1933. As our large construction program drew to a close, he was the recipient of many honors. The Edison Company paid him further honor, posthumously, when it arranged for the name of Florence Lake Tunnel to be changed to Ward Tunnel, and for the erection of an appropriate monument. The latter, built of bluish-grey blocks of tunnel granite laid in mortar, stands over the big pipe at the tunnel outlet. Imbedded in the granite is a copper tablet, bearing the following inscription:

Officials visiting Big Creek project, left to right, R. H. Ballard, George C. Ward, H. A. Barre, E. R. Davis with D. H. Redinger.

John B. Miller and his daughter Carrita have first ride on Florence Lake, August, 1926, piloted by the author.

.OUTLET OF

WARD TUNNEL

NAMED BY THE

SOUTHERN CALIFORNIA EDISON COMPANY LTD.

HONORING

GEORGE CLINTON WARD

1863-1933

WHO DIRECTED CONSTRUCTION OF THE ENTIRE
HYDRO ELECTRIC DEVELOPMENT OF THE COMPANY
ON THE SAN JOAQUIN RIVER AND ITS TRIBUTARIES.
THIS TUNNEL DIVERTS THE WATERS OF
MONO CREEK, BEAR CREEK AND THE SOUTH FORK
OF THE SAN JOAQUIN RIVER UNDER THE
KAISER RIDGE INTO HUNTINGTON LAKE.

CONSTRUCTED IN 1920-1925

LENGTH 67620 FEET

DIAMETER 15 FEET

CAPACITY 2500 CUBIC FEET PER SECOND

Mrs. Ward and their daughter, Louise Ward Watkins, were among those present on August 26, 1936, to hear W. C. Mullendore, Executive Vice-President at the time, deliver the principal dedicatory address.

XX

Florence Lake Dam

ALTHOUGH THERE WAS stream diversion—the South Fork of the San Joaquin River into Florence Lake Tunnel in 1925 —there was no storage at the site of the Florence Lake Dam, as the dam had not been constructed, and some legal matters were pending.

The site for the dam had been selected after extensive field studies beginning in 1923, which were supplemented by those in the office, dealing with quantities and costs. Various types of dams were investigated to find one suitable for the site and several estimates of cost were made with respect to selection of the most suitable and economical design. A rock-fill structure, using material from the Florence Lake Tunnel, and faced with either earth or asphalt-covered planking to make it impervious, was given extensive study with facing to be replaced by concrete after settlement. Various disadvantages were foreseen with such a type, and test pits in nearby meadows indicated a possible shortage of material for the earth covering. Adopted finally was the multiple arch, which estimates showed to be about ten per cent lower in cost than any other type. John S. Eastwood is credited with having originated and developed the first designs for a dam of that type.

In support of this selection were numerous important factors. The transportation of material from the rail head at Big Creek was a major item, and less cement would be required than for a gravity or part gravity structure—hence, less tonnage; the large amount of the steel needed for reinforcing could be supplied by using rail removed from the tunnel; concrete aggregate could be made by crushing the tunnel granite, examinations having shown it to be suitable; and, although more lumber for forms would be required, it could be supplied by our mill in the vicinity.

Full consideration was given to the possible effect of freezing temperatures on the concrete at that high elevation. It was felt that protection would be afforded by making concrete of highest quality and placed under the best methods known at the time. Furthermore, with Florence Lake empty, under normal operating conditions the concrete would be comparatively dry by the time freezing temperatures occurred.

A large rock-crushing and screening plant was installed at the damsite for making the various sizes of rock and the sand. To distribute the concrete an appropriate chuting system was constructed—the Insley chutes being suspended from two Insley steel towers several hundred feet in height—and the job was off to a good start, under the direct supervision of E. C. Panton, assisted by T. A. Smith, Anton Wellman, O. N. Kulberg, and other capable men. The first concrete was poured on March 4, 1925. To insure the best concrete possible, rigid inspection was provided which covered all phases—cement testing, batching, mixing, placing, testing concrete samples etc. A well-equipped laboratory was built near the dam, including a temperature-controlled moist-air curing room. The latter permitted concrete tests to be made unaffected by outside temperature. Some idea may be had of the extent of the tests from the number made—over eight hundred field samples and twelve hundred laboratory cylinders. The opinion is general, even today, that we went farther than was the usual practice to get a uniform concrete of highest quality.

The use of powder was generally avoided in the footing excavation for the arches, the "plug and feather" method being used largely to prevent shattering of the foundation granite. The forms for the concrete, difficult in some respects to make, were in panels on the upstream face, and carried up in four foot lifts. A hinged truss design was used for forms on the downstream side, matching in height those on the upper.

Being the longest dam of the type ever built—3,200 feet, and made up of fifty-eight arches—it attracted considerable attention from engineers, the general public, and, of course, the Edison Company itself.

Mr. Ward was, as always during construction, a frequent visitor. If there were a steam shovel in the vicinity, that's where he would be found. He would stand and watch one work for hours at a time. Other members of the top management from Los Angeles would visit the job occasionally, the most convenient time being the summer months. Roy Reppy, General Counsel for the Edison Company, paid us a visit whenever possible. He brought along on one trip, Jack Healy, a mining engineer and friend of long standing, who lived in South Africa. His strong English accent caused me to ask from what part of England he came. After sheepish glances at each other, Reppy said, "Don't let him fool you—he was born in Ventura." Long residence in Johannesburg had had its effect. In looking over the work on the dam, Healy's use of the word "shutters," several times caused me to inquire as to what he was referring. I learned that in South Africa that is what concrete forms are called, and "fitters" are the men who handle them, those whom we call "carpenters."

Enroute across the Pacific, I was talking to a fellow passenger registered from Johannesburg. Somewhat apologetically—since it is a large city—I asked if by chance she had ever heard of a mining engineer there by the name of Healy. Quick as a flash, she said, "Do you mean Jack Healy?" He had been her next door neighbor for twenty-five years. What a small world!

Mr. Reppy, besides his interest in the job, loved the outdoors, and enjoyed getting into khaki, high boots, an old hat, and a red bandanna around his neck. In such regalia he was in his element, and there was none better as a companion on a camping trip. I found President Story, of the Santa Fe, an excellent runner-up for him. Both men, gentlemen in every sense of the word, loved the mountains. It has been my experience that men, without exception, who like the wide open spaces, are very much worthwhile. Also, I know of no better way for men to really become acquainted than on a camping trip. If they cannot click after sitting around a camp fire together, there is not much hope.

We saw a great deal of H. A. Barre, who had much to do with the general scheme of the Big Creek development. With his unusual sense of humor, he had the uncanny knack of being able to see through a knotty problem, and would come out quickly with the answer—frequently in a facetious manner. A chain cigarette smoker, he remarked at various times that he might tackle a cigar if given one. I happened to come across a perfect rubber imitation of a "Perfecto," so I bided my time. Barre touched a match to it— a puff or two, and then Messrs. Ward, Davis and I got the real low-down on his opinion of the perpetrator of such a trick. I knew I was in for it sooner or later.

To enable him to carry out his "evil" design of revenge, he inveigled Mrs. Redinger into becoming his confederate. Two weeks or so later, I learned all about it, while I was all set to enjoy some weiners and sauerkraut, which he knew I liked. He had slipped into the kitchen a perfect rubber imitation of a nice juicy weiner, and certainly evened up the score.

The general design of the multiple arch dam was carried out by Messrs. Pierce and Heywood, under the supervision of Harry Dennis, who, with Harold Doolittle and their respective competent men, had their hands full for years in Los Angeles, with the plans, designs, lay-outs etc., for all the major jobs. Arthur Blight played a most important role as Assistant Manager of Construction during the program of major activity, the larger portion of his time being spent in the Los Angeles office. F. J. Mills, representing the Los Angeles engineering office, called on us frequently, and rendered valuable assistance with our construction problems—particularly with the Florence Lake Dam. Many of the designs worked out by Harold Doolittle reflect to the highest degree his most extraordinary ability, as, like Barre, he could see through a tough problem and quickly arrive at the solution.

Besides building the dam, we had to clear the reservoir of trees and undergrowth preparatory for storage. Our saw mill at Camp 61, having served its purpose in that location, was moved in 1925 and installed in upper Jackass Meadow, which was to become the reservoir. Camp 65 was established as the base for the mill operations and the clearing of the whole area. All trees large enough were run through the mill, the lumber being used largely in construction of the dam. For logging, we purchased three 60 Best tractors, the first of such equipment to put in appearance on our work. It was amazing what jobs the "cat skinners" found besides logging, and we wondered how we had ever gotten along without tractors. When the time came to move the Camp 63 buildings to higher ground, preparatory to reservoir storage, one of these tractors could yank a two-story bunk house to the new location, Camp 64, in short order. In one such structure, supposedly empty, a lone man from the night crew was asleep—but not for long—as it started bumping over the rocks. Half-awake, and not knowing whether the structure had been beset by an earthquake, he leaped out the window clad in his underwear, and hit the ground on the run. He had quickly decided he was not going places inside.

Looking for additional storage for the future, we sent a diamond drill to Blaney Meadows to make some exploratory borings for a damsite, having in mind possible storage there of 32,000 acre feet, but the study was later abandoned. "Lost Valley" is said to have been the first and true name for Blaney Meadows as early as 1870. In later years, a man by the name of Blaney grazed sheep there and, no doubt, is responsible for the name we know today.

Our courtesy cars were bringing visitors daily to see the dam as it gradually rose in height. The concrete skips running up and down in the high steel towers absorbed their attention. In fact, they were fascinated by everything. The central portion of the dam was of less height than the others, and could not be reached by the chuting system of either tower, so two traveling cranes were used to pour the concrete in that section. Many of our visitors were curious about the holes in the vertical face of a rock ledge not far from the dam. During tunnel construction, it had served as an ideal proving ground for trying out the drilling speed of various new machines, resulting in the large number of holes which puzzled the visitors. It occurred to the engineers to have some fun by explaining how the holes were made by "rock swallows," peculiar to that locality.

The largest saddle and pack train ever seen in those parts appeared during the summer of 1925, when the Simpson party left from the area we were clearing for the reservoir. James Simpson, Board Chairman of Marshall Field, Chicago, arrived with his party by private car in Fresno. I was asked to meet them, accompany them over the project, extend the usual courtesies, and see that they contacted the pack train. Col. John R. White, Superintendent of Sequoia National Park, joined in doing the honors, as he expected the party as guests at the end of their thirty-day pack trip. Even with Mr. Simpson's assistance, we had a tough time rounding up the scions of several prominent Chicago families after they had scattered in Fresno. From Big Creek, Mr. Simpson paid his respects by wire to Mr. John B. Miller, and eventually we met the huge pack outfit in upper Jackass Meadow. Getting the group on its way was as exciting as attending a big rodeo. After meals in our mess halls, the group would ask about gratuities to the help. I always told them this was not necessary. The party was well on its way, and excitement had died down somewhat, when I learned of the generous distribution of twenty dollar gold pieces! In fact, that was the smallest denomination handed out. It was with some difficulty that the gang got back to earth.

The time had come to close down the work on the dam for the winter. Sixty per cent of the concrete had been placed, the last for the season being poured on October 30, 1925. The cleared reservoir was ready to store water. The height to which the dam had been built would provide storage from the 1926 run-off for 35,000 acre feet—more than half of the ultimate capacity of 64,400. Concrete operations were resumed on April 29, 1926, and completed on August 15. Work continued on the final clean-up, such as hand-railing, back-fill, gate mechanisms, grouting etc., until November when the camp was closed.

Since water storage is of the utmost importance, it is highly desirable to know as definitely and as early as possible something about the water crop for each season. Irrigation needs are also important, besides those for power. If the latter are ample, the former will benefit, as the water is always returned to the river after passing through our Big Creek plants. Our storage reservoirs benefit the San Joaquin Valley by helping to prevent floods and regulating the run-off, distributing it over a longer period of time. To know what to expect in the way of a run-off from a water-shed, precipitation during winter months is of much concern, and is becoming even more so as the years roll by; consequently, beginning in the fall, much attention is paid to the weather. By spring, especially if the winter has been light, water becomes a topic of serious discussion. Many companies have, for years, in cooperation with the State and each other, conducted snow surveys at intervals during winter months. The depth and water content data obtained by these snow surveys at various locations produce more accurate results than precipitation, in estimating the water crop expected from the four hundred fifty square miles of watershed upon which our reservoirs depend for run-off.

Weather prophets have been found to be quite unreliable—even the Indians, who have been looked upon by the white man as something of a guide. A heavy winter was indicated if the Indians were seen laying in an unusually large supply of acorns, etc. M. A. Benedict, for many years Supervisor of the Sierra National Forest, is authority for a new version. When he asked an aged Indian who had lived near Forest Service headquarters for years what kind of a winter to expect, he received this reply: "Me think heap bad. White man, he get in much wood." Several years after hearing this from Benedict, I read the same story, but from another source, in the Saturday Evening Post.

The height of the arches in the dam, 147 feet, is greatest where they span the river. It is desirable to have some means for draining a reservoir below the level of its tunnel, which does not always take off from the lowest point. Two thirty-six inch sluice pipes in the bottom of the river span, each equipped with a forty-six inch square slide gate on its upstream end, hydraulically operated, permit drawing the water below the tunnel intake.

To provide for the release of water to sustain fish life in the river below the dam, a special eight-inch pipe and valve were installed near the main sluice pipes.

Reservoirs must also be equipped for safely releasing—that is, spilling—water above their capacity. In the Florence Lake Dam the spillway in the central section is one hundred feet long, the water being controlled by two fifty-foot drum gates. This type of spillway allows drift material to be carried over the gates with the excess water, and the lake level may be controlled by automatic or manual operation of the drum gates. Our practice has been mostly the latter, not taking any chances on faulty operation with the consequent loss of part of a full reservoir.

On the downstream side of the arches sufficient backfilling was done and drainage provided to keep water from standing against the concrete in freezing weather. Some backfill at the base of the arches on the upstream side was placed for the same reason when the lake would be empty. In spite of efforts to produce concrete of highest quality possible, it was not long after completion of the dam before the effects of freezing were recognized. The water from snow melting on the walkway would run down over the concrete in the daytime and was followed by low temperatures at night. No doubt some of the trouble was due, too, to the concrete being more or less wet as the lake level went down. Many theories have been advanced about this frost action on concrete that causes it to spall—flake off—or disintegrate. It has been a most puzzling problem for years to engineers who have tried to reach the root of the trouble and make concrete which would not be vulnerable to freezing temperatures. Is it due to some unfavorable characteristic of the aggregate, the cement, the water used for mixing, or some combination of all three? The method of distributing the concrete may have been a factor.

Attention was given to some means for waterproofing the upstream face of the dam. Studies resulted in the application of "Inertol," a German formula, in 1926, which did not prove very satisfactory. In the early '30's, a covering of emulsified asphalt was applied. Through the years to date, considerable maintenance has been necessary to retard the spalling, which has been greatest on the walkway, buttress heads, and upstream face of the arches and angle buttresses.

During the war years, we were at a considerable disadvantage because of the limited field for waterproofing materials. The application of "Asbestile," with some yearly maintenance, has been on the whole more or less satisfactory, but it is not considered to be the final answer. Many different materials have been investigated in the laboratory, including the "Asbestile," which was selected as it had the advantage of being reasonable in cost, as well as in application, and was not a strategic war material. One arch has been covered with steel plates, welded together, and applications of gunite have been made on other arches, on the spillway, walkway, and buttress heads. As to what the final answer will be, time may tell.

A program of long-time study has been undertaken by the Portland Cement Association, in cooperation with many interested companies, including ours, the State of California, the U. S. Bureau of Reclamation, and others. Official inspections and tests are made at least once a year of specimen concrete bars, walkway sections made of different brands of cement etc., on the Florence Lake Dam. Many cores have been cut from the arches for testing. Linseed oil as a protective coating is being tried on walkway sections. Light-reflecting paint, to hold down temperatures from the sun, has been applied on the arches. All such efforts may some day lead to the adoption of some material or method as the satisfactory solution for present concrete troubles. With intensive efforts, progress has been made in the past fifteen years in the manufacture of cement, and more has been learned about the aggregate, proportioning, mixing, and placing of concrete.

Mr. John B. Miller made his last visit to Big Creek in 1926, bringing his daughter Carrita. They were the first visitors to enjoy a ride on Florence Lake. I can still see the expression of satisfaction on his face as he sat in the boat with Carrita and me, puffing on his pipe and scanning the body of water stored for the first time.

Stretching the imagination, one might have noticed an expression of approval from Mt. Shinn, overlooking the newly-made lake. This prominent pyramid-shaped mountain was named by the U. S.

Forest Service, honoring the memory of Charles Howard Shinn, first
supervisor of the Sierra National Forest, which was established as
"Sierra Forest Reserve" by proclamation of President Harrison on
February 14, 1893. Additions were made under the present name
by President Theodore Roosevelt, in his proclamation of April 20,
1908.

Keeping Mt. Shinn company is Ward Mountain, officially named
for George Clinton Ward by action of the Division of Geographic
Names, Washington, D. C. The attractive bronze marker standing
near the west end of Florence Lake Dam and pointing to Ward
Mountain, was dedicated appropriately on August 26, 1936, following a similar ceremony for the monument at the outlet of Ward
Tunnel.

Florence Lake Dam and reservoir.

Above: Bear Creek Dam and reservoir, November, 1927.

Left: View looking southwest on Mono Bear Siphon project, 1927. Rugged, uneven terrain made laying of siphon one of most difficult accomplishments of Big Creek project.

Right: Link-belt shovel is used as crane to lay Mono-Bear siphon.

XXI

Diversion of Mono and Bear Creeks

WHILE THE Florence Lake Dam was being built, and even before that, extensive studies were being made for new sources of water for additional power. The rapid development of power resources in the Big Creek area came as a result of the remarkable growth in industry, business and population throughout the territory served by the Edison Company. This condition has continued up to the present, 1949. The opinion was general that a lull could be expected after the World War II years, but so far, it has been just the opposite.

During the '20's, our new plants and additional units in the existing plants were rushed to completion in an effort to keep pace with the power demand. Not previously mentioned are the following additional units that were installed: a third unit in Power House No. 2 in November, 1920, and a fourth during April, 1925; in Power House No. 1 a third unit was added in July, 1923, followed by a fourth in June, 1925. These four increased the installed capacity in the two plants by 110,500 H.P.

The possibility of storage in Vermilion Valley was being explored, diamond drill borings being made for a damsite. The lower end of the Valley—the logical location for such a dam—is crossed by several terminal moraines left by the glacier as it receded.

F. J. Mills, with his usual philosophic outlook on things, opined that, apparently, the Creator had placed material for the toe of the dam on the wrong side of the site. This recalls to mind another instance in which Mr. Mills played an important part. At the time we were building Plant No. 3 on Kern River, there were indications that the shale formation back of the location for that power house would require a retaining wall. Mr. Brackenridge, Senior Vice-President then, Harry Dennis, Mr. Mills and I, besides a few others, met on the hillside to discuss the situation. Except for Mr. Mills, we thought we noticed a twinkle in Mr. Brackenridge's eyes, as he turned and asked, "Mr. Mills, why did you put the power house in this location?" After a few seconds of silence, Mr. Mills replied, "Because that is where you told us to put it." There was another short interval of silence before Mr. Brackenridge asked him, "What would you do if I asked you to turn the flow of the river out there, upstream?" Without any hesitation, Mr. Mills replied, "Mr. Brackenridge, if you gave me such instructions, I certainly would do my damnedest."

Mr. Brackenridge was not as well known to our Big Creek personnel as others of the top management, since he made only a few visits to this area.

The decision ultimately reached favored a small concrete diversion dam on Mono Creek and one on Bear Creek, both streams to be carried across the South Fork of the San Joaquin River through a steel siphon, emptying into the Florence Lake Tunnel at the Camp 62 Adit. To accomplish this, the means had to be provided to get both streams into the siphon. One tunnel through hard granite had to be built from Bear Creek to converge with the shorter one from Mono Creek at the intake of the long siphon.

The "80" series of numbers was assigned for the camps established for the construction. Camp 80 was built near the site for the Mono Dam; 81 at the intake of the Mono Tunnel; 82 at the intersection of both tunnel outlets, where the siphon would connect; 83 and 84 along the siphon; 85 at Bear Creek tunnel adit; and 86 at the Bear Creek damsite.

Between six and seven miles of road had to be built through the worst terrain imaginable. Boulders the size of houses, and huge ledges of the hardest granite, were encountered. Steep grades and sharp turns resulted from dodging such obstacles. The routes appeared to be almost impossible, since many large trucks would have to be used for the delivery of material. It is amazing what men with determination, portable air compressors, jack hammers and powder, can accomplish when once started. The "C. and N."—Cheap and Nasty—road was completed, camps made ready, and work on the conduit got under way in July, 1926. Winter caused stoppage of activity on November 24, and it was resumed again in the early spring of 1927.

A 1¼-cubic yard Link-Belt gas-operated shovel was purchased for use largely as a crane for placing the siphon pipe sections. To reach the job early, we used it in May, 1927, to dig its way over Kaiser Pass through snow six feet deep, and of course, in doing so, it opened the road for all traffic.

Many people have asked about the origin of the name "Kaiser," given to the Pass and Peak. In spite of efforts to find out, all I have been able to learn is that the name is very old and the correct spelling unknown. L. A. Winchell reports hearing miners speak of Kaiser Gulch in 1862—hence, maybe, the name "Kaiser Diggings."

As one travels beyond Kaiser Pass towards Florence Lake and emerges from the timber one sees Mt. Ritter towering above others in the distance. This is the name of the German geographer, Karl Ritter. This lofty peak, it is reported, was approached from the southwest by Clarence King about 1866, in an unsuccessful attempt to reach the summit.

The remote Mono-Bear camps were not without their virtues. There were excellent opportunities for fishing. The "Ike Waltons" enjoyed such advantages, and a trout dinner at any camp could be had on short notice. In season, there was venison for those desiring a change in meat diet. I recall having bear meat at one meal. Even though scarce, bears have always raised havoc with hydrographers' supplies stored for intermittent trips in remote cabins unless protection somewhat comparable to a bank vault is provided.

We were paid a visit by a special Government representative named Welch, from Washington, D. C., who was sent out by the Secretary of the Interior to visit our national parks. During his visit here, and while being shown around by E. R. Davis and me, he related an interesting experience with some local cattle men. I cannot vouch for his veracity in this respect, but he told it on himself. He had always wanted to get into some western cattle country and take a trip with cattle men. After being out several days with them when they were taking a large herd into the back country for summer grazing, he was caught off his horse one afternoon by a large steer. Apparently, the steer had taken a dislike to this individual for some reason or other. Being unsuccessful in reaching his horse, Welch jumped into a hollow tree, the nearest place of safety. The steer ran around the opposite side and Welch came out—only to be chased in again. This performance occurred several times before the cattle men came to the rescue. One suggested to their guest that he should have stayed in there until help came. Welch replied, "Stay in there, Hell—there's a bear in there."

Two small concrete arch dams, one on Mono Creek and the other on Bear, were built for stream diversion only. Sluice pipes and valves were installed as is customary, and means provided to release water for fish life below. The diversion conduit from Mono Dam to the head of the siphon consists of a ninety-two inch steel pipe line, about three-quarters of a mile long, connecting into an eight by nine foot tunnel of approximately the same length. The Bear Creek branch is also about one and one-half miles in length, but all tunnel, part being seven by seven feet, and part eight by nine feet—meeting the

Mono Tunnel at the siphon intake. The siphon, three miles long, varying in diameter from seventy-five inches to one hundred and two inches, has a capacity of six hundred cubic feet per second, and carries the water across the South Fork of the San Joaquin River into the Florence Lake Tunnel.

The Mono-Bear tunnels were too small for the use of our regular mucking equipment. To facilitate the loading of the cars, Tunnel Foreman Ed McCabe, who had been on the Florence Lake Tunnel, improvised the "McCabe Mucker." This contraption elevated the muck and dumped it into the cars. The men had to shovel it onto the endless belt, but this method was easier and faster than hand-shoveling into the cars, as they would have had to raise the muck four or five feet.

The excavation for the siphon was made mostly through hardest granite, a sizable job in itself. The blasting echoes from the tunnels and siphon excavation reverberated through the canyon like the sound of huge guns on a terrific battle front.

Russell Booth, one of the assistant engineers, was in direct charge of the job during the greatest activity, which was in 1927.

Big trucks, as many as twenty-five in service at one time, hauled the steel pipe sections from the top of the main incline at Huntington Lake to the site, where the Link-Belt shovel, as a crane, unloaded and placed each in the proper position in the trench. In general, things clicked like clock work.

There was a big question as to whether or not the siphon, especially, and Mono flow line, should be back-filled—that is, covered. No precedent could be found to satisfy those concerned that there would be no trouble from ice in the pipe unless it was adequately covered; anchor ice forming on the inside could cause much trouble. The only safe thing to do was cover it—a huge job— but this was done to a minimum depth of three feet. Recording thermometers were installed at several locations along the siphon the first winter, and results indicated that satisfactory operation, free from ice trouble, could be expected. The intakes at Mono and Bear are submerged to eliminate trouble with ice at those points. Strange as it may seem, there has been nothing of consequence to develop on either of these small dams in the way of the concrete spalling, as has occurred on other structures at high elevation. Just why is a question.

The Mono-Bear job was completed on November 15, 1927, and diversion started into the Florence Lake Tunnel, ending another important unit in the development of power resources in this area.

The major activity beyond Kaiser Pass having come to a close, the Edison Company in 1929 turned over to the Government, through the U. S. Forest Service, the Florence Lake Road, also abandoning the one to Mono-Bear. In recent years, the Forest Service has oiled the road from the upper end of Huntington Lake to Florence, and a flourishing concession, a motel, with store and cottages, has grown up at Mono Hot Springs. With mail service during summer months, and a public camp ground established by the Forest Service near Mono Dam, one appreciates the extent to which once remote mountain areas are being made available to the motorist.

XXII

Shaver Dam and Power House 2A

EVEN THOUGH Florence Lake Dam had been completed, the reservoir would not provide storage for all the run-off of the South Fork of the San Joaquin River. Neither could Huntington Lake store the excess in addition to the run-off from its own watershed, plus that from Mono and Bear Creeks. This situation was fully understood and taken into consideration in planning.

During the period between purchase by the Edison Company of the Shaver property in 1917, described in a previous chapter, and 1925, careful studies were made involving that portion, 2,200 acres, that would be suitable for a reservoir, and its co-ordination with the entire Big Creek development. By 1925 the studies had resulted in final plans for storage of the excess water from the Florence and Huntington Lake watersheds, plus its own, in the new reservoir to be provided by the construction of a large concrete, gravity-type dam at Shaver.

As is usually the case, several sites for a dam were explored before final selection. There are always many factors to be considered from the standpoint of economics, especially when it comes to deciding on the capacity of a reservoir and the type of dam to be built. The gravity type, stable because of its own weight against the water pressure, would have a maximum height of 183 feet above the bedrock, a thickness of about 125 feet at the base, and length of nearly 2,200 feet along the crest. Such a structure would provide storage for 135,000 acre feet, plus, of water.

Much had to be done preparatory for construction of the dam—"spitting on one's hands," as Herb Barre said. A huge amount of cement and lumber would be required, besides all other material common to a job of such magnitude—though in comparison to several dams built since, its 280,000 cubic yards of concrete are not so significant.

To serve the job, we built 4.6 miles of standard gauge railroad from Dawn, where connection was made to the main line of the San Joaquin & Eastern, from which H. L. Wheeler was borrowed to supervise construction of the branch, and to open and handle the rock quarry. Early in May, 1926, construction started on the large rock-crushing plant for making the concrete material, including sand, all of which was to come from the quarry to be opened on the side of a granite cliff a short mile distant. To keep the hungry crushers fed from the quarry was Hank Wheeler's job, the rock to be transported by trolley locomotives over a narrow guage track. Today the quarry "scar" is pointed out to visitors as the place "where the Shaver Dam used to be."

While stock piles of the various sizes of crushed material grew in size, excavation to bedrock at the damsite was progressing. It was worked towards both ends from the center, and continued ultimately to the extent of about 150,000 cubic yards, half of it being in solid rock.

Two steel towers were rising high in the air to support the counter-balanced chutes of the concrete distributing system. The concrete mixing plant was taking shape, and finally the bank of three large Smith mixers was ready to perform. The last concrete in the Florence Lake Dam having been poured, the entire crew moved from there to Camp 21 at the Shaver damsite. Everything was in readiness, and the first concrete was poured onto the foundation on September 21, 1926. Because of freezing weather, operations were discontinued on December 4 and resumed April 1, 1927.

The dam was built in fifty-foot blocks, with a construction joint between each. Besides the usual key-way at each joint, a thin copper sheet about thirty inches in width extends from top to bottom, spanning the joint to make it water-tight. The sheets were placed in ten to twelve foot lengths, lapped and brazed at the ends. Concrete expands and contracts with temperature changes, and to allow the copper sheets to withstand the slight movement of the huge blocks without breaking, they were corrugated, or "V" shaped in the center.

Another feature provided in the dam is the large gallery running through most of its length, a short distance above the foundation. Its twelve-foot height was to permit the later operation of a diamond drill for holes which would relieve pressure from possible seepage water. Water will find its way through crevices in the foundation rock in spite of precautions to seal them by grouting. It will also work its way, more or less, through a day's work joint and even around a construction joint. Such a gallery provides the means for periodic inspections also. The one in the Shaver Dam is the only one among the dams on the Bg Creek project. Several years later, another and shorter gallery was excavated along the contact of the concrete and bedrock for purposes of observation.

The largest mess hall on the project, seating several hundred men, took care of the "inner man," and sleeping quarters upstairs accommodated those who were not allocated to bunk houses.

Another big job, clearing the reservoir site, was handled by Bretz Brothers, local men, who programmed their work to have the site ready for storage as the dam approached completion, which occurred on October 23, 1927. Between April and August 1 of that year, an average of 1,431 cubic yards of concrete was placed, the maximum for one day being 1,808.

The elevation of the spillway in the central portion of the dam— 5,370 feet above sea level—sets the mark for high water. Although the reservoir has been full during various years, there has been no appreciable spill allowed—the storage, diversion and use being controlled by operating conditions in the reservoirs above.

Some means had to be provided to control the flow of water from the reservoir for use in the power house far below in the Big Creek Canyon. A vertical shaft, about one hundred feet in depth, was excavated near the north end of the dam to tap the Shaver Tunnel, and a nine-foot gate was installed at the bottom, operated by an electric motor in the intake house on the surface, with a gas engine for emergency use.

With completion of the Shaver Dam and clearing of the reservoir, one of the last things to be done was the removal, by burning, from the reservoir area, of all structures that remained—including the old saw mill, store, and surrounding buildings. In the final cleanup of the store and postoffice, we found a sizable box of gadgets which no one could identify until Mr. Ferguson, "Fergie," of Clovis, an old-time employee of the former lumber company, was called on for assistance. Apparently, the rest of us were too young to have recognized the contents of that box as oxen shoes. To fit the hoof of an ox, the shoes, of course, had to be in two halves, a right and left piece.

The County road—it had not yet been taken over by the State— had to be changed as it passed over the old rock-fill dam and by the Shaver Store. We built the road as it is today, about two miles in length, winding below the dam and joining the old highway opposite the rock quarry.

Several years before the reservoir clearing started, the Sulphur Springs area served another important purpose as a golf course for Edison employees. Early in 1923, spurred on by O. J. Schieber and Vallery White, golf enthusiasts, practically every employee spent his days off helping clear fairways and making sand "greens" for a nine-hole course. The wives were just as much interested as the men, and did their part in the preparation of many picnic lunches and dinners. The employees built a club house, and the finest in the land could not have furnished more pleasure. For those who needed lessons in the game—and most of us did—there was a "pro" available; and he was a busy "bird," too. Many of those who became proficient in handling the little white ball continue in the sport today elsewhere, crediting their beginning to the Shaver golf course. It was with much regret that we dismantled the club house and played our last games in 1926, to make way for what is today the greater Shaver Lake.

The expression of regret by others was even greater in the passing from the scene of an old landmark—the hallowed quarters of the Shaver Lake Fishing Club. The old building had for many years been the rendezvous—for two weeks each spring—of Fresno business and professional men. Each outing ended with the annual dinner and "Hi-Jinks." "Chef" Eddie Jones, known to many travelers as the popular "red cap" at the Southern Pacific Station in Fresno, had for years prepared the annual dinners deluxe, and he did his stuff for the last one, which in some respects would have caused George Rector to sit up and take notice. The dinner lasted for hours, including stunts by the top "jinksters." General Mueller, a grand old gentleman and dean of the group, sat at the head of the table with his big sombrero on—a privilege enjoyed by him only. One guest, a bit tipsy, apparently felt sorry for the group lamenting the impending loss of the quarters, and poking his head through an open window, attempted to toast those at the long table, addressing them as members of the "Fisher Lake Shaving Club." The closing ceremony was impressive, as well as somewhat pathetic, when a torch was applied to the building while all sang "Auld Lang Syne." For several years thereafter, the club held its meetings in quarters made available in the resort camp built by the Edison Company, and which was the forerunner of what is now "Johnny's."

The yearning for a building of their own was too great, and the club built its own quarters, which it now enjoys, practically isolated on the southern shore of the Lake.

The Shaver Lake area must have been frequented in times past by Indians, as many arrow heads, spear heads and countless beads have been found by members of our Big Creek personnel. Emery Morrison, who has become quite an authority on the Indian lore in this vicinity, has built up a huge collection from his annual searches after the Lake has been drawn down.

During his last visit to Big Creek in 1926, Mr. John B. Miller, with his daughter Carrita, wished to camp out in the Shaver reservoir area. It was my pleasure to share their enjoyment for two days and nights in the special camp we had established. Before going to sleep, Mr. Miller would lie on his cot and talk about the wonderful progress he had seen through the years, how interesting it had been to watch his company grow to what it was at the time, and envisage even more greatness for the not too distant future.

To utilize the water to be stored in Shaver reservoir, and as a part of the general scheme of development, a new power house called "2A" was started in June, 1926, while we were getting ready to build the dam. It is located adjacent to Plant No. 2, both being operated as one. The water for the former plant is diverted through the Shaver Tunnel, previously described. The first unit of the new plant went into service during August, 1928, followed by the second in December. The total head of 2,418 feet, under which both units operate, is one of the highest in the United States, and exerts a pressure on the water wheels of more than a thousand pounds per square inch. Each generator, with an operating capacity of 46,500 kilowatts, is driven by double over-hung impulse wheels, or turbines —the largest of the type, 63,000 H.P. operating capacity—installed anywhere in the world at the time. The penstock, longer than for any other plant in the Edison system--6,712 feet—connects to the

Shaver Dam and reservoir, partly full.

Big Creek Powerhouses No. 2-2A at night, 1947.

Shaver Reservoir when full.

outlet of the Shaver Tunnel, varying in diameter from one hundred and eight inches at the top to sixty-six near the power house. The water must be carried to each water wheel—hence the two 48-inch branches, each of these branching into two 24's. An interesting feature involving the three huge "Y" pieces, reinforced by heavy steel bands, is that they were made by the once great Krupp Works in Germany. Riveted pipe, made locally, constitutes the upper portion of the penstock. The banded forge-welded central portion was made in Poland, and the bottom section, forged and seamless, was made in this country.

In a previous chapter was some description of the spalling of concrete on the Florence Lake Dam. As the years have passed since the Shaver Dam was completed, there has been disintegration taking place on it, but to a lesser degree—though the walkway along the crest has had to be refaced completely.

Disintegration was progressive on the Huntington Lake dams before and after they were increased thirty-five feet in height. We noticed, from many observations, that this condition had not occurred where the concrete was protected by a cover of earth. During the '30's a major job of backfilling was done, covering each structure on the downstream side with a heavy layer of earth, followed with one of rock to prevent erosion. More recently, backfill has been applied to lower portions on the face of each, Dam 1, restricted by the tunnel intake, receiving the least. When the original excavation was made for the Huntington Lake dams, the material was piled below each structure in several large "spoil" banks. These grew considerably in 1917 from the additional excavation preparatory to increasing the height of the dams. Years later, when Mr. Ballard was president of the Company, he thought those below Dam 2 were unsightly for Huntington Lodge guests, and on several occasions made comments to me, not realizing the expense involved to remove them. Eventually, they became part of the backfill. One day as Mr. Ward and I were walking across that dam, pointing to the "spoil" banks, I mentioned Mr. Ballard's comments. He listened most attentively, then, with a twinkle in his eyes, said, "If Ballard kicks any more, you tell him he doesn't know a damned thing about it." "Mr. Ward," I replied, "I am sure you can imagine me saying that to Mr. Ballard." Whereupon he added, "All right then, tell him I said it." Before the subject came up again, I was in attendance at an annual meeting of the Edison Company in Los Angeles, and Mr. Ballard, who was presiding, called on me to say something about Big Creek. Among other things, I told the above story—much to the delight of Edison Company executives, particularly Mr. Ballard. After the meeting, Mr. Ward wanted to know if I was trying to get him fired.

XXIII

Huntington-Pitman-Shaver Conduit

IT HAS BEEN MENTIONED previously that Shaver Lake reservoir would provide storage for excess water which could not be held in Florence Lake and Huntington, the run-off from its own watershed not being sufficient to fill it. The Shaver storage is affected by use and distribution of water from the upper watersheds, as load conditions of the Big Creek plants govern such factors.

Means had to be provided to get the excess water from Florence and Huntington Lakes into Shaver reservoir. Early in 1925, we started work on the Huntington-Pitman-Shaver conduit for such diversion. Roads had to be built and camps established. The "70" series of numbers was assigned to the project, with Camp 71 at the outlet portal of the short tunnel below Dam 2; Camp 72 at the only adit; and Camp 73 located at the outlet portal of the long tunnel above Shaver. Eleven miles of road from the north end of the Shaver area were built to serve the two latter camps.

By November, 1925, actual work on the tunnel got under way, efforts being concentrated on the longer section to be worked from Camp 72 to 73. We were in need of mucking equipment for the new tunnel. Messrs. Blight, Kruger and I visited Moffatt Railroad Tunnel in Colorado, spending several days observing all operations in driving the huge bore and the small water tunnel paralleling it. As the result of that trip, we ordered several Conway mucking machines for our job, and they proved to be quite satisfactory.

Camp 73 was the headquarters for the work carried on at the outlet portal, and also at Camp 72, about three miles distant by road. The camp included a base hospital, in charge of Dr. W. N. Carter, but it was on a much smaller scale than any of the others we had had elsewhere.

Besides the 4.8 miles of 14-foot by 13-foot horseshoe-shaped tunnel, the conduit consists of about 3,200 feet of 8 to 10 foot steel, riveted pipe. A short section of the latter goes through Dam 2 at Huntington Lake, and connects to the short tunnel leading to the long 10-foot steel siphon, which extends across Big Creek Canyon to the tunnel, whose outlet is at Camp 73.

In all references to "siphon," such as this and the Mono-Bear, it should be understood that an inverted one is indicated, and not the true type. Water passes through the inverted siphon by its own pressure, the intake being higher than the outlet. The 10-foot pipe through Dam 2, near its base, serves as the intake for the Huntington-Pitman-Shaver conduit. In driving the hole through the dam, the concrete was broken piece by piece by the "plug and feather" method, as the use of powder was not allowed. Two gates control the flow from Huntington Lake into the conduit—a 10-foot one on the face of the dam, supplemented at the upper end of the short flow-line by an 8-foot duplex, its two leaves for opening and closing sliding horizontally.

Pitman Creek water is dropped into the main tunnel upstream from Camp 72 adit through a deep shaft. This Creek, as reported by L. A. Winchell, received its name from a rancher who lived below Tollhouse and had a hunting cabin on its banks in the early days.

Considerable trouble was encountered with bad ground in the tunnel about two miles upstream from the outlet at Camp 73. A major cave-in had occurred, eventually causing a large crater-like depression on top of the mountain. It was necessary to abandon a portion of the tunnel, back up, and go around the bad area. In doing so, we did not miss it entirely, but succeeded in getting through with the use of heavy timbering, which was followed later by a lining of reinforced concrete. Repairs had to be made to this section in the winter of 1944-45, with a steel-reinforced gunite section, as cracks in the original concrete indicated fatigue from ground pressure. To reach the tunnel for these repairs, the Camp 72 adit, being the nearest approach, had to be rebuilt as it had caved in through the years. Stone & Webster did all the repair work. Another by-pass while driving the main tunnel, to dodge more bad ground, had to be made where a cave-in extended to the surface upstream from Pitman Creek shaft. We had a most interesting experience in the outlet heading; quite some distance from the portal, after a round had been blasted, the flattened root of a pine or fir tree was found in a granite crevice, the shortest distance to the surface at that point being 450 feet. Undoubtedly, the root had followed the crevice to water.

Camp 72 suffered the worst disaster in the history of the Big Creek development—the snowslide which struck about two o'clock on the morning of February 15, 1927, followed by another about seven a. m. causing the death of twelve men and one woman. A heavy snow storm was raging, and all telephone lines were down. As far as can be learned, the only member of our present local personnel who experienced the slides is Leo Robinson, who was shop foreman at Camp 72 at that time. The corner of the bunk house in which he was sleeping was torn away, but he escaped uninjured. He and Art Kocher, the latter then connected with this office, are authority as to how the first report reached Big Creek headquarters. T. L. "Red" Coff, a lineman, made the arduous two-mile trip through the deep snow down the mountain side. Kocher had the local siren sounded about 4:30 a.m., after which hurried steps were taken to render all possible aid. It was ten days before all bodies were recovered. During the gruesome search far down the mountain, one group of men reported seeing a canary fly out after they had burrowed deeply into the snow and debris—no doubt having come down with the family residence. I was in China at the time, and did not learn of the disaster until after I arrived in Tokyo. In none of the mail from Big Creek written after February 15 was there any mention of it, the news having been omitted intentionally. On my first visit to the Tokyo Club, I was anxious to see a newspaper from my own country, and the first thing which struck me like a brick was the big headlines in a month-old San Francisco paper.

Enroute back across the Pacific, I learned further details from Mr. John B. Miller, who, with Mrs. Miller, and their daughter, Carrita, was vacationing in Honolulu. After a final fling at Waikiki, we returned to San Francisco on the same ship. I enjoyed breakfasts aboard with Mr. Miller, always finding him at the early table. The second day out from Honolulu, his cabin boy looked me up on deck, as Mr. Miller was anxious to know if by chance I had any "JBM," his favorite smoking tobacco—mine too—on hand. Fortunately, I did. I had used little, as the sea, quite rough at times, did anything but create a desire for me to even smell tobacco, let alone smoke it. Needless to say, the remainder of the trip—for Mr. Miller, at least—was made much more pleasant. The "JBM" brand, from his initials, was originated by him, so he had told me years before. The clientele of the Los Angeles Spring Street tobacconist who handles it includes as devotees of that brand the names of many prominent men in this country, and up to World War II, some in foreign countries. Any smoker could not help but be tempted after reading the label. On each can appear two pictures—one of Big Creek Power House No. 1, and one of No. 2. Besides these, there is the following:

Conway mucking machine at Camp 72 in 1926.

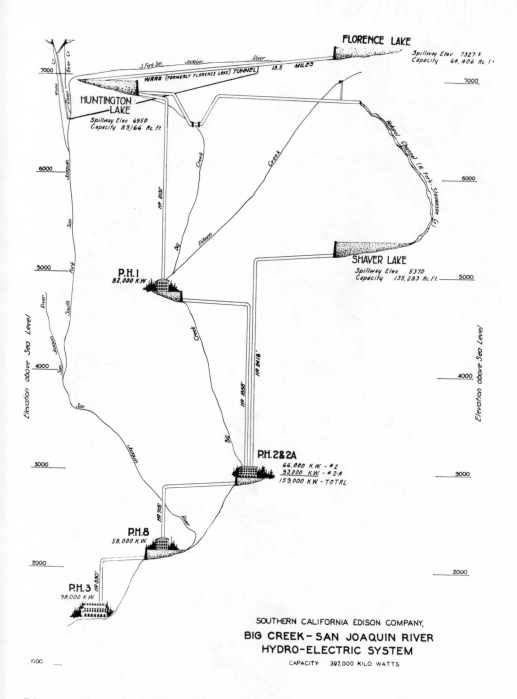

FLORENCE LAKE
Spillway Elev. 7327.5
Capacity 64,406 Ac. Ft.

WARD (FORMERLY FLORENCE LAKE) TUNNEL 13.5 MILES

HUNTINGTON LAKE
Spillway Elev. 6950
Capacity 89,166 Ac. Ft.

SHAVER LAKE
Spillway Elev. 5370
Capacity 135,283 Ac. Ft.

P.H. 1
82,000 K.W.

P.H. 2 & 2A
66,000 K.W. - #2
93,000 K.W. - #2-A
159,000 K.W. - TOTAL

P.H. 8
58,000 K.W.

P.H. 3
98,000 K.W

SOUTHERN CALIFORNIA EDISON COMPANY,
BIG CREEK—SAN JOAQUIN RIVER
HYDRO-ELECTRIC SYSTEM
CAPACITY 397,000 KILO WATTS

Diagrammatic profile of Big Creek development. Capacity has recently been increased by addition of 30,000 kilowatt unit at Big Creek No. 3 in 1948.

"HUGUNIN'S JBM MIXTURE"
This mixture is prepared from old Burley
leaf, especially selected, aged for five
years in wood, stripped by hand, bound
with Canadian maple sugar, and blended
with Fragrant Hollandish.

No attempt is intended here for advertising this product. It is mentioned solely because of its association with Big Creek. Although not a heavy pipe smoker, I have kept a supply on my smoke-stand for years—ever since its originator introduced it to me. I never enjoy a pipeful without a recollection of the pleasant memories connected with its unusual background.

While in Japan, I was amazed at their engineers' familiarity with our Big Creek plants. Of course, many had visited not only Big Creek but other major installations throughout the United States and they had certainly made the most of their opportunities in collecting data for use in their own country.

Work on the Huntington-Pitman-Shaver conduit was completed on April 21, 1928, when diversion into Shaver Lake from Huntington began.

With completion of this conduit and Power House 2A the same year, and with the addition of a second unit in Big Creek 8 in June, 1929, all major construction for that period came to an end, making Big Creek, with its 533,000 H.P. operating capacity for the turbines, and 398,000 kilowatts for the generators, the largest hydro part of the Southern California Edison System. Although other power houses had been planned, the proposal to build Hoover Dam caused our picture to change, and the Edison Company joined forces in helping with that development by agreement with the United States Government to assume its share of electric power.

On the Big Creek Project, about thirty-six miles of tunnels have been driven. At various times, several of us made trips to visit such

projects as Hetch-Hetchy, Don Pedro, Exchequer and Balch, to
see what the other fellows were doing in the construction of their
dams, power houses and tunnels. While in New York during construction of the Holland Tunnel beneath the Hudson River, I had
my first experience under compressed air, when I was escorted
through the air locks and down to the huge shield by the Chief
Engineer, Cliff Holland, for whom the tunnel was named. Admit-
tance of visitors was kept to a minimum, largely because of the
conditions which they would encounter. Such under-water tunneling has to be carried on under compressed air to counteract the
pressure from above and keep the water from breaking through the
mud and clay into the workings. The air pressure really holds Death
at arm's length. A medical examination was required of every
visitor, to ascertain his condition to withstand the high air pressure,
which reaches as much as thirty-eight pounds, depending on the
amount necessary to equalize that exerted from above. Men and
material go through air locks—huge steel tanks—in which the
pressure is gradually raised to equal that on the working side.
Going from normal to high pressure air takes about three to five
minutes. After the lock is closed by the steel door, a valve is turned,
and one can not only hear the air hissing but feel the pressure
increasing. When the desired pressure is reached, the steel door in
the opposite end of the chamber, or lock, is opened and one steps
out into the high air. With me, I felt a pain in my neck, literally,
beneath both ears—and was most uncomfortable. Reverse passage,
coming from the high pressure side out to normal, called decompression, takes much longer than going in—up to forty-five minutes.
The men who work behind the huge shield, which is forced ahead
through the mud and clay by many powerful hydraulic jacks, are
known as "sand hogs." Slow decompression is of vital importance
to prevent the much-dreaded disability among sand hogs known
as "the bends." They wear dog tags for identification, as an attack
of the bends may be suffered when one is off duty and out on the

street. Treatment consists of rushing the victim to the nearest compression chamber and then allowing decompression slowly. The bends comes from working under compressed air, where large amounts of nitrogen are absorbed in the blood stream. It is supposed to be eliminated as the sand hog passes through the decompression chamber, or lock. Otherwise, the nitrogen forms bubbles in the body tissues or bloodstream, causing the various symptoms of compressed air illness, such as pains in the joints or muscles, and in the neck. Sand hogs cannot remain at work long under high air; consequently, their shifts are short, with rather long intervals in between. The plant for supplying compressed air to the section visited was in triplicate, I observed, each unit of compressors being complete in itself and having a source of power entirely independent of the others, and any one bank being capable of furnishing the required pressure. Should the pressure in the working get too low, water and mud would rush in upon the workmen. On the other hand, should the pressure get too high, they might be blown through the mud and water to the surface. I was told that although both kinds of accidents had actually occurred, they were few and far between. In spite of such dangers, the sand hogs continue to ply their trade, putting their faith in the engineers who plan and design such undertakings. I have often wondered how many users of the tubes beneath the Hudson, regardless of the method of transportation, ever give a thought to the dangers and hardships undergone by those involved with their construction.

In the summer of 1927, we were paid a visit by a group of men from Italy, and to whom we have referred as the Hydro Electric Commission from that country. It appeared to compare somewhat with our own Federal Power Commission. The Los Angeles Office asked me to meet these gentlemen personally upon their arrival by train at Big Creek. Hurriedly I looked around, trying to find an Italian from one of our tunnel crews who could serve as an interpreter. The group was due before I met with any success, so I had to make the best of it. I sized up each man as he stepped off the train, and decided to take a chance with the one I thought to be spokesman for the group. Very much to my surprise, each individual greeted me in better English, perhaps, than most of us use ourselves. While entertaining them at Huntington Lake Lodge during their stay here, I told them of my concern, and asked how it is that practically each and every foreign visitor we have either speaks English fluently, or enough to get along without much difficulty. They told me, speaking for themselves, that they had studied English because it was their desire some day to visit the United States of America, and when that happened they wanted to be able to speak the language. Foreigners put most of us to shame when it comes to the matter of languages.

Engineers, especially, have been here from all over the world. Engineers, however, are not the only ones to be credited with knowing languages other than their mother tongues. In September, 1936, we had as guests a large number of delegates, mostly foreigners, to the Third World Power Conference held in Washington, D. C. Two special train loads came west. At Fresno they split into groups for visits to various localities, including Big Creek. There was little need for interpreters. The Fresno County Chamber of Commerce gave a big dinner the evening all had returned from the day's outings. Seated on my left at the banquet was a gentleman from Uruguay, with another on my right from Chile. Both spoke English fluently and, of course, Spanish. After my complimenting them on their use of the former, they conversed briefly with each other in French, for my benefit. During the day I had asked an Italian gentleman who had been riding with me, questions about Italy. After looking around to make sure no other member of the party was nearby, he answered in a low voice, "You should thank God you don't have a Mussolini in your country."

XXIV

Stevenson Creek Test Dam

NO DESCRIPTION OF THE Big Creek development would be complete without including something about the Stevenson Creek Test Dam, which attracted considerable attention in the engineering world during the time it was being built, tests made and reports prepared. No attempt will be made to go into the technical details of that program, but it is felt a general description is justified.

Prior to the early '20's, there had been much discussion among engineers and others concerned, about the design and cost of arch dams in power development, water supply, irrigation, flood controls etc. Involved was the question of whether such structures were being over-designed, with a consequent waste of construction materials, to say nothing of the extra cost. Up to that time many arch dams had been built in this country, some in Australia, and others were scattered over Europe. There had been no reports of failure. Engineers had no real experimental knowledge to support design theories. Some dams had been built thick and others thin. In the former, there might have been more material than necessary, and in the latter the limit of safety could have been closely approached. Throughout all discussions of the subject, uppermost in the minds of engineers especially, was the permanence and safety of the structures.

In 1922, Fred A. Noetzli, a consulting engineer in Los Angeles, acting on behalf of engineers on the Pacific Coast and in the Rocky

Mountain states, prevailed upon the Engineering Foundation to undertake a study of arch dams. The "Engineering Foundation" is an organization which functions under the direction of several of the larger national engineering societies, and is devoted specifically to research along engineering lines. As previously mentioned, many hydraulic projects involve the arch dam as a major item in development; therefore, it is extremely important to all concerned that its design be on the same scientific basis as all other parts of the entire development.

In December, 1923, Mr. W. A. Brackenridge, then Senior Vice President of the Southern California Edison Company, suggested that an experimental arch dam be built—one comparable to some of those in existence at the time. A suitable site had to be selected, one where there would be no interference with its construction, or, as a result of the numerous tests contemplated, with anything else. Mr. Brackenridge offered on behalf of the Edison Company not only contribution of funds, but also facilities and a site in Stevenson Creek Canyon, mid-way between our Big Creek Plants No. 3 and No. 8. Stevenson Creek, a tributary of the San Joaquin River, is the natural outlet for Shaver Lake. The site would provide the desired small reservoir capacity, and allow tests to be made safely, even to the destruction of the dam with a full reservoir. All such tests would be made under field conditions.

The program adopted was a practical endeavor, scientifically directed to get facts from experiment and experience, all for the better guidance of engineers in the design of arch dams. There was a feeling on the part of some engineers that the data to be obtained would justify some changes in the design of arch dams, with a corresponding reduction in cost without jeopardizing the safety of such structures.

The experimental program was endorsed by the Federal Power Commission and the State Railroad Commission of California.

The United States Bureau of Standards cooperated whole-heartedly, and assigned its Mr. W. A. Slater to be on hand during construction of the dam, and to remain for supervising tests, collecting data and preparing reports. Other Government bureaus and agencies rendered valuable assistance in many ways. Mr. Brackenridge was appointed sole trustee for collection and distribution of funds. The Edison Company started contributions with $25,000 towards the ultimate cost, estimated at $100,000. The cooperation of others to be benefited was invited. Many companies throughout the United States responded with cash donations, or equipment, material and supplies. H. W. Dennis, of the Edison Company, supervised the construction of the dam, with R. C. Booth, of our local engineering personnel, in charge on the ground. The investigation committee, headed by Charles D. Marx of Stanford University as chairman, included, besides Mr. Dennis, several other well known engineers in the Pacific Coast area.

By November 1, 1925, the necessary camp and facilities had been made ready and the work got under way. By April 1926, the excavation for the foundation was complete and ready for concrete, the first pour being made on the 19th. By June 4, the structure was completed to the present height of sixty feet.

During construction of the dam many instruments were imbedded in the concrete, and metal plugs and reference points carefully set for taking various measurements. According to Mr. Slater, one hundred and forty electric telemeters were scattered throughout the dam, buried in the concrete. Their purpose was to measure microscopic changes in length and temperature within the instruments themselves, by means of varying electrical resistances. Definite data were wanted on just what was going on inside the dam after the concrete had set, in the way of strains from expansion, contraction etc. The electric telemeters used were designed by Messrs. McCullom and Peters, of the Bureau of Standards. As stated by them, the electrical telemeter "depends upon the well known fact that if a stack of carbon plates is held under pressure, change of pressure will be accompanied by a change of electrical resistance and also a change in length of the stack." By the proper interpretation of the resistance readings registered by the telemeters, it was possible to obtain the desired data. Lead wires extending from the telemeters permitted readings to be taken at a convenient distance from the dam. The wires ended at a terminal board so that all readings could be taken at one location.

During World War II, engineers from the United States Army visited the site, having in mind the feasibility of using the structure for testing the destructive power of explosives under water and close to concrete dams. Nothing further ever came of that investigation.

Various measurements and observations were begun with the first steps of construction. For test purposes, water was first allowed to build up behind the dam to a depth of twenty feet in July. Extensive tests were made with water twenty feet deep, and at ten foot intervals up to and including sixty feet—top of the dam. With each test a full series of measurements were made, with the small reservoir filled to the desired level, and with it empty. To take advantage of the least change in temperature, these tests were made at night. Under load tests, according to Slater's report, no crack occurred in the dam proper with a depth of water less than fifty feet, but under this head one occurred on the vertical center line, extending entirely through the dam from the downstream face to the upstream face, and down to an elevation of about forty-nine feet on the downstream face. Another crack appeared under a head of sixty feet of water on the vertical center line of the dam, extending from two inches above foundation rock to a height of about nine feet—and extending itself later to a height of thirteen feet. Each of these cracks was first discovered by means of the telemeter readings. The last load tests made started with the reservoir full—a sixty foot depth—and continued at ten foot intervals down to and including the thirty foot level, the water being lowered accordingly.

The Committee reported some tentative conclusions in its Volume No. 1, subject to modification in Volume No. 2, to be submitted to the Engineering Foundation at completion of the work. The Committee felt that with the aid of the information being compiled from the test data, measurements and observations, arch dams of less thickness than would formerly have been considered necessary could be built on some sites. As far as I know the second volume was never finished because of Mr. Slater's death. The St. Francis Dam disaster in Southern California probably had some effect towards making any radical change in the design of all dams, even though the failure was not caused by a fault in the design of the dam itself. One thing the Stevenson Creek Test Dam did demonstrate is the great strength of a thin, reinforced, concrete arch dam, provided it is well built on a proper foundation.

Interest in the investigation was world-wide, particularly among engineers, as previously indicated. There have been many visitors to the dam, including some engineers from foreign countries. Even today, there is seldom a visitor to the Big Creek Project, engineer or otherwise, who does not ask about the test dam—and who, if time permits, does not want to see it.

XXV

Improvements in Equipment

IT HAS BEEN INTERESTING to observe the changes and improvements that have been made, both in construction equipment and otherwise, on our job from 1912 to the present time. Along with these have come improved methods in construction.

Teams and scrapers, along with wheelbarrows, played the major role in building the San Joaquin and Eastern Railroad—in fact, they did so in the early construction of the large railroads we know today. The amount of material moved by a well organized crew of men with wheelbarrows, "Irish Buggies," teams and scrapers, handled by real "skinners," was amazing. Today, wheelbarrows are used only where nothing else is practical, and men scoff if they are not fitted with pneumatic tires and roller bearings. Having used both the old and new types myself, I do not blame them. Even shovels, "muck sticks," have been improved in shape and material. Mule skinners who know their stuff are scarce today, and so are men who really know how to push a wheelbarrow.

In the old days, the mule skinners would feed the animals on their way to breakfast so they would be ready for the harness after the skinners had eaten. The teams would be on the job by 7:00 o'clock. With the advent of the truck, instead of "twisting the mules' tails," the skinner would crank the engine, and be reminded frequently of a mule when the crank would kick back. Today, merely stepping on the starter eliminates even that hazard.

The one automobile on the Big Creek job in 1912 did not even

Stevenson Creek Test Dam, 1926.

Helicopter lands on The Point on first trip to Big Creek, to be greeted by excited residents.

Sno-Motor with sled on way to Kaiser Pass, with O. N. Kulberg of engineering department as passenger.

have a truck for company. Trucks did not begin to replace horses, mules and wagons until along towards 1920, although passenger cars were becoming more numerous in the meantime. Our large stables were eventually replaced by garages, the heavy and light wagons, along with a few cars, were gradually pushed aside by various types of automotive equipment. Although there are a large number of horses and mules today, they are restricted largely to cattle ranches, riding stables, dude ranches, and packing concessions in the mountain area. It is difficult to find among members of the younger generation one who can harness a horse, let alone hitch it to a vehicle—if a horse-drawn one could be found—but they have considerable knowledge of an automobile. What a lot they have missed!

Automotive equipment took over completely for general use during the '20's. Tractors without dozers put in their appearance in 1925 at Florence Lake, for use in our logging operations. It was not long before they were equipped for work as bulldozers. The more maneuverable crawler steam shovel showed up during the earlier '20's to replace the railroad type, which was restricted to use on railroad tracks. In recent years, the smaller shovels come mounted on a truck chassis, and can be moved quickly from place to place.

For moving large quantities of earth we have used the huge carry-all, towed by a tractor. As compared to the old dump wagon and even the present-day dump truck, the carryall not only gobbles up a mouthful of several cubic yards, but can carry it almost any distance before disgorging, leveling it besides. Along with such earth-moving equipment is that ingenious device, the sheep's-foot tamper, used where necessary to pack a fill instead of hand tamping. The huge roller is covered with hundreds of small steel projections resembling sheep's feet. We are told the idea was developed as the result of someone actually observing the effect from the feet of hundreds of sheep driven over a large fill—hence the name for the tamper.

The four-wheel drive truck, "F. W. D."—without any discredit to its cousin that is driven only by the rear wheels—will, as the men say, almost climb up the side of a building. Such equipment renders incalculable service, especially in snow and mud. I have had my car towed—it is more correct to say, "dragged"—over a road, while the truck's wheels were buried above the axles in mud.

In our early tunnel driving, we were plugging along with the heavy, clumsy and slow piston air drill, until the lighter, faster and more efficient air hammer put in its appearance between 1914 and 1920. Tunnel drill steel was sharpened by hand before the arrival of the air-operated drill sharpener. In the old method, the helper certainly earned his money wielding the heavy sledge hammer, while at the same time developing some husky muscles. Along came the oil furnace for heating drill steel instead of using coal and coke, and as is usually the case in adopting anything new, the old timers were somewhat skeptical, but were slowly weaned away from coal and coke and the air blower forge. Tempering drill steel requires skill; a man may be expert with a drill sharpener, and fall down badly on tempering. Nothing exasperates the operator of an air hammer drill more than improperly tempered steel.

The faithful mules, too, were pushed aside when the electric locomotive came along to pull the muck cars.

To keep pace with these improvements in driving tunnels, the use of fuse for blasting gave way to the modern method of doing it electrically, with all the holes in the heading being connected to an electric circuit and the exploders detonated when the master switch, at a safe distance, was closed. The firing of the holes in proper rotation was determined by the time exploder placed in the charge of each.

We had no snow-removal equipment until the tractor came along.

During the '20's, a special piece of equipment—it could be called a "rotary," mounted on a truck chassis—was given a trial on the road between Big Creek and Huntington Lake, but without success. A home-made V-shaped scraper, towed behind a truck, worked very well for the removal of light snow. With it as a starter, a heavy one with hydraulic lift was made and fitted around one of the tractors. The tractor really sat inside the frame and pushed the plow. Another tractor was fitted with a heavy blade equipped with a hydraulic lift. A bulldozer can move deep snow provided there is room along the roadside for the snow to be rolled over and down a bank. The present-day rotary snow plow, or "Sno-Go," as it is called, as used by the State Highway Department, has proved to be the most satisfactory type of equipment for snow removal. It moves along slowly through the deep snow and throws it in a heavy stream, clearing the entire roadway.

Some means had to be found for traveling over the snow other than on foot, snowshoe or skis. The first contraption tried out was motor-driven, and was supposed to be pushed ahead over the snow by a revolving worm shaft in the rear, on the order of the screw conveyor used for moving wheat in large elevators. Instead of pushing the outfit ahead, it would bury itself by digging straight down. One of our small tractors was fitted with specially made wide wooden tracks, but without success. It would go only so far, and when the snow got too soft and deep would "sit back on its haunches"—in other words, rear up with the front end up in the air and the rear burying itself by digging down to the road.

P. H. Ducker, who has headed the transportation department of the Edison Company for many years, was on the look-out for something that would travel satisfactorily over the snow. He arranged for the purchase of our present "Sno-Motor," a crawler-type piece of equipment designed by T. P. Flynn, snow equipment engineer of the U. S. Forest Service. It arrived here on February

3, 1941, and was taken on its trial trip the following day, from Big Creek to Kaiser Pass and return. Its operation was quite successful, and it has rendered excellent service for seven winters in the transportation of men and material over the snow. The main unit operates much the same as the well known Caterpillar tractor, except that it has only one endless crawler tread which extends across the entire width of the machine, fifty-six inches, and travels completely around it. A long sled, which is towed, furnishes the fulcrum for turning. Without the sled, the machine can move only forward and backward. Steel plates four feet long, on either side of the sled, cut down into the snow, providing the means for steering—much the same as a rudder on a boat. Thirty-percent grades, and probably some steeper, have been easily made with a full load of two and one-half tons. Powder snow on grades causes some trouble, but an experienced operator will compact a trail by forward and backward movements of the machine. The Sno-Motor fulfills a long-felt need for winter transportation in our high, snow-bound regions. Ours was the fifth one in use in the United States at the time of its purchase.

Hydrographic work in this area keeps expanding, and requires frequent trips in both winter and summer by hydrographers to remote stations. A lighter piece of equipment, smaller than the Sno-Motor, was needed for traveling over the snow. Mr. Ducker arranged for the purchase of a Tucker "Cat"—we call it "Sno-Cat" —made by E. M. Tucker, of Grass Valley, California. It provides good transportation for two men, along with a reasonable amount of such equipment as hydrographers carry. The Sno-Cat is equipped with crawler-type treads in the rear, on both sides. In front, pneumatic-tired wheels may be raised or lowered to alternate with skis, as conditions require.

Only some of the major improvements in construction equipment have been described. One can only conjecture what the saving in time and money would have been in such a huge development as this had they all been available since 1912.

Aerial photography accomplishes wonders as compared to the survey parties formerly needed on reconnaissance. In a few hours, a photography plane can cover an area that would require the arduous work of a survey party for weeks and even months. It should be said, however, that pictures taken from the air must be carefully interpreted by an expert to obtain the desired data for final field location.

Electric ranges did not come into general use by employees in this area until the early '20's. When the free use of electricity was discontinued, all employees going on meters, there was a sudden decrease to the extent of seventy-five percent in the amount used— another example of the oft-repeated comment, "People do not appreciate anything they do not pay for." Front porch lights became conspicuous by being turned off during daylight hours.

Even though this area is in a national forest, there is pretty much of a wood famine of late, because of the difficulty of getting it—no one wants to cut it and few know how. Hence, the use of fuel oil has become the general practice.

The Engineering Construction Pay Roll #45, which had served many thousands of employees for many years, finally came to an end. The last one to be transferred from it was H. A. Barber, of the present local engineering staff, on November 1, 1931.

This chapter should end with one last story involving visitors, thousands of whom, as already mentioned, have been here during the busy construction years and since. During the Golden Gate International Exposition, while I was having lunch in San Francisco with two chief engineers, the engineer for the Golden Gate Bridge was curious to know whether I had ever been asked a foolish question by any of our visitors. I told him of the individual who wanted to know how we got the water back into Huntington Lake after it had passed through the power house! The Oakland Bay Bridge engineer thought he could go one even better. He had spent part of a day escorting a group over the two big bridges, winding up with a trip through the large Exposition buildings. While visiting the latter, he had emphasized the fact that all were to be dismantled at the close of the Fair. When saying goodbye to his party, one lady, who had displayed unusual interest in all the sights, said, "It's bad enough to think about the removal of such lovely buildings, but what really makes me sick is the thought of tearing down those two wonderful bridges."

XXVI

Retrospection

THE GLAMOUR OF THE big construction job has disappeared, but to most of us who went through it there will always remain pleasant memories. Now and then someone asks if I have not grown tired of my long stay here. If one is really interested in his job and has good health, time does not hang heavily and he keeps reasonably contented. It matters not where one finds himself, there are always advantages and disadvantages. For a place like Big Creek it makes a difference, too, when one loves the mountains. Although the big construction job was more interesting and fascinating, much satisfaction has been derived from directing the operation of the project—the result of many years' effort by thousands of men, and one which has added so much comfort for millions of people.

There has always been enough variety to prevent monotony—visitors of note who were keenly interested, and who, in turn, added much from their own experiences. Trips in connection with the job, as well as for recreation, provided welcome changes, although for a while vacations were irregular because the job was too interesting or too important to leave.

During the '30's I enjoyed being a member of a special consulting board of engineers, with the Metropolitan Water District of Southern California, on an assignment having to do with driving the San Jacinto Tunnel, an important link in the Colorado River Aqueduct.

Looking back through the years, one of the things that stands out most clearly in the whole picture is the human element—those who made the completion of the big job possible—men like Mr. Ward, Mr. Miller and Mr. Ballard, who had the vision, the ability and the confidence to go ahead in spite of many difficulties. I mention Mr. Ward first since he had full responsibility for the huge construction program. Fortunately for all three men—each, in turn, was President—they were able to see the completion of the big job before they passed on. The Sunset Club of Los Angeles had a heavy bronze tablet placed on the east end of Power House No. 1, honoring both R. H. Ballard and George C. Ward, and bearing the following inscription:

THE SUNSET CLUB OF LOS ANGELES

PROUD OF THE PART TAKEN IN THIS MIGHTY ENTERPRISE

BY TWO OF ITS MEMBERS

RUSSELL H. BALLARD AND GEORGE C. WARD

PLACES THIS TABLET HERE

IN GRATEFUL ADMIRATION OF THEM

AND THEIR ASSOCIATES

TO LIGHTEN THE DARKNESS OF MULTITUDES AND

TO SPEED THE WHEELS OF HUMAN PROGRESS THEY

SMOTE THE MOUNTAINOUS ROCK AND LIVING WATERS

RUSHED TO DO THEIR BIDDING

A. D. 1929

There were others, too, who, while not so outstanding perhaps, played a most important part in their respective places—men like Charlie Scott, "Doc" Dwight, T. A. Smith, Bert Wilson, "Sandy" Gilzean, "Scotty" Lawson, H. A. Noble, and last but by no means least, "Jumbo"—these gave their all and were still "in the harness" when their time came to pass beyond. They, and others like them, gave their utmost in devotion and loyalty, their one idea being to see their respective jobs done, without regard to overtime, holidays or vacations, when their services were needed. I wonder, sometimes, if they did not get something from their work and a job well done that, perhaps, the average man never experiences. I recall emergencies and how these men responded—sometimes when their own best interests, physically and otherwise, made it inadvisable. Besides being a good veterinarian, "Doc" Dwight was one of our best "cat skinners." Once while sick in bed, he learned of a vital trip to be made through deep snow, and when the large tractor left, "Doc" was in the seat, realizing he was the best qualified for that particular job. Until the day of his death, "Scotty" Lawson, who had come along the hard way, found it difficult to take overtime pay, saying that it was his duty, and if he could not do his job within eight hours it was up to him regardless of time—nights and holidays made no difference. "Jumbo" (Jevto Vasilovitch), huge of stature, had no "book larnin'," but he did have a natural know-how and the strength for doing unusual things—an excellent runner-up for Hercules himself. T. A. Smith, an excellent all-around construction man, never faltered, even during those days when he should have been in bed—men less interested in their jobs would have been. It is not possible to mention more than a few of the many men deserving credit, but nothing could be written about the major Big Creek construction without including the name of Mark Gunderson, who, as master mechanic, played a most important role. Unfortunately, he lived to enjoy only a few years of his justly earned retirement. Many were the difficult and complex problems which arose to confront him and H. A. Noble, his successor, and due credit must be given both for their unusual skill and ingenuity in handling each and every one. Both were among those unsung heroes who had no regard whatever for the clock, giving their all unstintingly to help get the big job done and to keep it running afterwards. Heman Noble passed away almost on the eve of his retirement.

I am not unmindful of the wives of employees, who did a wonderful job, too, through the construction years and since. Some lived in tents, some in cottages of more or less temporary nature, and others in more permanent quarters. All deserve much credit for standing by their husbands and providing so many of the comforts of home. It was much more trying for the wives, because the husbands had the interesting features of a huge job to hold their attention and keep them occupied, while the wives had the usual house work, along with the inconveniences and handicaps common to most camp life.

Having viewed this section of the country from a regular plane, traveled over it on snow shoes and skis, by horse and wagon, on horseback, by dog sled and automobile, and under it through many miles of tunnels, it was my pleasure to be taken on the first flight of a helicopter over Huntington Lake on July 16, 1947. The take-off was made from "The Point." The ship rose easily, and the landing reminded me of a setting hen settling down carefully on a nest of eggs. The helicopter trip really rounded out an unusual program of diversified means of travel. Time certainly marches on!